Disability, Intimacy, and Sexual Health

A Social Work Perspective

Kristen Faye Linton, Heidi Adams Rueda, and Lela Rankin Williams

D1600212

NASW PRESS

National Association of Social Workers
Washington, DC 20002-4241

Kathryn Conley Wehrmann, PhD, MSW, LCSW
President

Angelo McClain, PhD, LICSW
Chief Executive Officer

Cheryl Y. Bradley, *Publisher*
Stella Donovan, *Acquisitions Editor*
Julie Gutin, *Project Manager*
Julie Palmer-Hoffman, *Copyeditor*
Julie Kimmel, *Proofreader*
Lori Holtzinger, Zinger Indexing, *Indexer*

Cover by Suzani Pavone, Eye to Eye Design Studio, LLC
Interior design, composition, and eBook conversion by Xcel Graphic Services
Printed and bound by Sheridan

First impression: October 2017

Library of Congress Cataloging-in-Publication Data
Names: Linton, Kristen Faye, author. | Rueda, Heidi Adams, author. |
   Williams, Lela Rankin, author.
Title: Disability, intimacy, and sexual health : a social work perspective /
   Kristen Faye Linton, Heidi Adams Rueda, and Lela Rankin Williams.
Description: Washington, DC : NASW Press, [2017] | Includes bibliographical
   references and index.
Identifiers: LCCN 2017029799 (print) | LCCN 2017039861 (eBook) | ISBN
   9780871015235 (eBook) | ISBN 9780871015228 (pbk.)
Subjects: LCSH: People with disabilities—Sexual behavior. | Intimacy
   (Psychology) | Sexual health. | Social work with people with disabilities.
Classification: LCC HQ30.5 (eBook) | LCC HQ30.5 .L56 2017 (print) | DDC
   305.9/08—dc23
LC record available at https://lccn.loc.gov/2017029799

Printed in the United States of America

Contents

Foreword

"I hope he has a good sex life." More than 25 years ago, I heard these words from a mother of a teenage son with cognitive and physical disabilities when I asked her what her greatest hope was for her child. Not a job, not a safe and secure living environment, but a good sex life. In its purest forms, sex affords a degree of intimacy, tenderness, and vulnerability that define, in some important way, what it is to be human and what we as humans so desperately require to thrive.

In this groundbreaking work, Kristen Faye Linton, Heidi Adams Rueda, and Lela Rankin Williams step into this taboo topic and provide guidance for social workers and other helping professionals working with people with disabilities. This text provides the reader with a unique and unparalleled synthesis of Linton and her colleagues' own research with a wealth of existent findings, historical context, policy directives, and practice guidelines to shine light on this challenging and complicated issue. As noted in chapter 2, society's historical approach to addressing the issues of sexuality among people with disabilities has been fraught with oppression. Many people with disabilities were forced to undergo procedures designed to deny and impede any expression of sexuality, including mass sterilization and castration. The growing recognition of the sexuality of people with disabilities might be considered a natural outgrowth of the continuing march toward full community inclusion launched more than 40 years ago with deinstitutionalization and the disability rights movement.

The interplay among self-esteem, social relationships, and sexuality during childhood and the development period has been well documented. Chapters 3 and 4 provide the reader with an examination of the normative experiences of relationships, friendships, and intimacy that children and adolescents with disabilities face. The authors note that during this period growing self-awareness of being different and challenges in establishing friendships can have devastating effects on the self-esteem and mental health of young people with disabilities. For parents of young people with disabilities, venturing into the topic of sexuality with their child can present unique challenges. Chapter 5 provides a terrific summary of research regarding the status of sex education for people with disabilities and offers some excellent resources for the social worker.

The authors then go on to address some of the more significant concerns emerging from sexuality among people with disabilities, including victimization; considerations of the parenting demands of women with disabilities; and, finally, considerations of marriage, cohabitation, and the resulting impact on disability benefits. The juxtaposition of interview extracts and Bronfenbrenner's (1977, 1979) ecological systems theory, a tool that the authors use throughout this text, provides the reader with a familiar orientation to consider the various topics. The authors conclude with an examination of the special issues associated with sexuality and aging.

For readers new to working with people with disabilities, and for those who have struggled to provide support to their clients regarding their sexuality, this text serves as a thoughtful, well-developed, and considerate primer to an important topic. I wish that I had had the benefit of this text many years ago, as I started my own career of working with people with disabilities and their parents.

Michael S. Shafer, PhD
Arizona State University

About the Authors

Kristen Faye Linton, PhD, is an assistant professor of health science at California State University, Channel Islands, in Camarillo. Prior to her research career, she spent over a decade as a social worker, supporting people with disabilities and their families to live independent, fulfilled lives in the community. Her research focuses on disability and health disparities with particular attention to sexual health, brain injury, race, and ethnicity. Her education and experience as a social worker and qualitative and quantitative methods researcher has prompted her to conduct community-based intervention research and evaluation that responds to community needs.

Heidi Adams Rueda, PhD, is an assistant professor at the Department of Social Work, University of Texas at San Antonio. Her research focuses on adolescent dating and sexual relationships within ecodevelopmental contexts, particularly among understudied youth populations including Mexican American youths, pregnant and parenting youths in foster care, and adolescents with disabilities. Within a holistic approach to dating health, her work aims to prevent teenage dating violence and to foster strong foundations for healthy adolescent and lifelong partnering. She uses mixed methods to inform the design and evaluation of effective preventative interventions and social work practice with adolescents.

Lela Rankin Williams, PhD, is an associate professor and coordinator at the School of Social Work, Arizona State University, in Tucson. Her interdisciplinary training in psychology and human development and family studies is informed by an ecological perspective, including the importance of regarding cultural and familial relationships as meaningful contexts within adolescent romantic relationships. She is committed to the development, evaluation, and implementation of culturally meaningful youth-driven prevention and intervention programs. As an active leader in both academic and community settings, she places a high priority on conducting rigorous and culturally relevant research in collaboration with community partners that is both meaningful and accessible.

Acknowledgments

Kristen Faye Linton and Heidi Adams Rueda began this project to fulfill requirements for a course in the PhD program, with mentorship by Lela Rankin Williams, at Arizona State University. We never dreamed that the small beginnings of this study would result in peer-reviewed articles, conference presentations, and a book. We could not have done this without the contribution of the 42 social workers across three states and eight people with disabilities who took time from their busy schedules to share their experiences and knowledge with us. We are also thankful to the MSW students who conducted interviews and contributed to data analysis: Alex Sandoval, Andrew Reding, Eva Pesta, Sharon Bolin, and Emily Hops.

Our education on this topic started far ahead of the beginnings of the study. We cannot forget the many clients we served who shared their stories with us. The most heartbreaking were those of sexual victimization in childhood, struggles with domestic violence, and coercion to give up a newborn because of a diagnosis of intellectual disability. However, we were also encouraged by the smiling, giddy faces of people looking forward to dates and the inspiring stories of strong, committed marriages. This book is dedicated to those clients we served.

We want to thank our families for their support throughout the years of this project. Thank you for your patience and unwavering loyalty. Heidi, who was diagnosed with chronic fatigue syndrome in 2012 and continues to work daily on her recovery, extends heartfelt gratitude to her husband and to her international online community for their healing love and support. You inspire and motivate us to want to make the world a more inclusive environment for all people.

1

Disability and Sexual Citizenship

For decades, people with disabilities have been physically segregated from others in separate classrooms, schools, and, in some cases, institutional living facilities. However, a topic given less attention is their sexual segregation and lack of *sexual citizenship*, which is defined as a "belonging" and "acceptance in wider society" (Weeks, 1998). Although progress has been made over the years to address public and educational accommodations, intimate relationships and the sexual rights of people with disabilities remain taboo (Americans with Disabilities Act, 1990 [42 U.S.C. 12101 et seq.]; Individuals with Disabilities Education Act [IDEA], 2004 [P.L. 101-476]). People with disabilities are commonly perceived as "asexual," and if they exhibit sexual behavior, it is often viewed as less acceptable, unsafe, or inappropriate (Murphy, Elias, & Council on Children with Disabilities, 2006; Shandra & Chowdhury, 2012). Research demonstrates that people with various disabilities have just as much, if not more, experience and desire for sex and intimate relationships than others (Donenberg, Emerson, Brown, Houck & Mackesy-Amiti, 2012; Löfgren-Mårtenson, 2011; Mandell et al., 2008). However, their rights to obtain sex education and receive support to have safe sex and intimate relationships

1

are limited by both informal and formal practices and policies (Swango-Wilson, 2011; Tissot, 2009).

This book explores the intimate and sexual health needs of people with disabilities through the perspectives of the social workers who work with them. Using the life course and ecological systems perspectives, we interviewed social workers serving people with a range of disability types and levels of severity. In sharing the experiences and perspectives of social workers, we give voice to advocates of those with disabilities. We talked to social workers serving children, adolescents, adults, and older adults across a variety of practice contexts, including child welfare, adoption, school social work (including those working at specialized schools for specific disabilities), medical social work, private practice, family support agencies, forensic social work, and nursing homes—in essence, those who understand firsthand the gaps, stigma, and disenfranchisement this population faces in their everyday lives. Our findings reflect those of the National Association of Social Workers (NASW), which found that between 75 percent and 88 percent of social workers support people with chronic medical, neurological, physical, and developmental disabilities (NASW, 2006). Despite this finding, very little specialized education is provided for social workers even though it is required by the Council on Social Work Education (CSWE) 2008 educational policy and accreditation standards (Bean & Krcek, 2012; Laws, Parish, Scheyett, & Egan, 2010; Quinn, 1995). Thus, social workers are left to make decisions at their discretion using the guidance of their generalist social work practice education and the NASW (2015a) code of ethics. Because of limiting organizational and governmental practices and policies, such as abstinence-only policies in schools or rules that prohibit cohabitation in supportive housing for people with disabilities, social workers often face ethical dilemmas while supporting people with disabilities to meet their intimate relationship and sexual health needs.

As social work scholars and practitioners, we are dedicated to ensuring that social workers are equipped to empower people with various disabilities to safely experience sexual behaviors and intimate relationships. Similar to CSWE's (2008) accreditation standards, we believe that disability is an element of diversity rather than a pathology. This lens challenges the medical model of disability and does not see disability as an inferiority. Rather, we hope to equip social workers to view disability through a strengths perspective that simultaneously views disability as similar to other elements of diversity (for example, race, ethnicity, gender, age) and recognizes unique challenges faced by people with disabilities that require special consideration and service delivery.

We originally conducted a phenomenological study of 13 school social workers' perspectives of the intimate and sexual health needs of adolescents with disabilities. A phenomenological design meant that we prioritized social workers' voices in communicating their experiences and the meaning they gave to those experiences (Padgett, 2008). We were inspired by these social workers' depth of exploration on the topic, dedication to their clients, and determined call for additional resources to address the needs of people with disabilities. Thus, we expanded our scope to include a total of 42 social workers who supported people with disabilities throughout the lifespan in various roles in three southwestern, southern, and West Coast states. The social workers we interviewed described the intimate relationship and sexual health needs of people with disabilities in various stages of life, the roles they held, and their recommendations for practices and policies to address their needs. They also spoke extensively about their own needs across systemic levels in supporting people with disabilities toward greater sexual and relationship health. Interviewing social workers serving children ($n = 13$), adolescents ($n = 13$), adults ($n = 11$), and older adults ($n = 5$) enhanced the rigor of our findings by assessing the extent to which themes were transferable across settings and served as a form of methodological triangulation by offering different types of information on the same topic (Padgett, 2008). Social workers also represented different self-reported genders (female = 31; male = 11), races and ethnicities (white = 26; Hispanic = 6; more than one race or ethnicity = 5; black = 2; Italian = 2; and Asian American = 1), and education levels (PhD = 1; MSW = 36; BSW = 5).

In addition, using phenomenological design, we interviewed eight young adults between the ages of 22 and 29 years with various mental health, physical, intellectual or developmental, and learning disabilities and asked them to reflect on their experiences with intimacy and sexual health. We share passages from these interviews along with those of the social workers to give voice to people with disabilities themselves. They also represented different genders (female = 5; male = 3) and races and ethnicities (white = 5; Mexican American = 2; Ghanaian American = 1).

One of the authors, Kristen Faye Linton, has over a decade of experience supporting people with various disabilities across the lifespan. Heidi Adams Rueda and Lela Rankin Williams bring specific expertise in romantic and sexuality research, especially pertaining to vulnerable and ethnic minority youth populations. Thus, this book was developed from a combination of clinical practice and research. The reader will take from it a better understanding of the issues encountered in social work practice among people with disabilities. As consumers of research, they may also develop their own sense of inquiry around this subject matter as many questions are left unanswered in the academic literature. Finally, as advocates, they may feel a tug within their own professional lives to advocate across multisystemic levels for change that is required to meet the sexual and intimate relationship needs of people with disabilities.

The structure of this book is inspired by the social workers' acknowledgment that the intimate relationships and sexual development of people with disabilities are influenced by their immediate settings (microsystem), the interactions between those settings (mesosystem), settings in which the person is not always present (exosystems), and cultural patterns in society (macrosystem), which is indicative of Bronfenbrenner's ecological systems theory (1977, 1979). Social workers often serve in micro- and mesosystemic roles, although we also include attention to exo- and macrosystemic influences. We include many examples throughout, providing direct quotations from social workers as often as possible to reflect the meanings they conveyed.

Disability is widely defined because it is not uncommon for social workers to work with people with various and often co-occurring disabilities. The Americans with Disabilities Act (1990) broadly defines *disability* as a physical or mental impairment that limits one or more major life activities. References to specific disabilities were consistent with diagnoses defined by recent editions of the *Diagnostic and Statistical Manual of Mental Disorders* (American Psychiatric Association, 2000, 2013) and IDEA

(2004). Brief definitions of disabilities will be provided, yet social workers are encouraged to learn more about these disabilities in the fifth edition of the *Diagnostic and Statistical Manual of Mental Disorders* (DSM-5) and IDEA. Because interviews were conducted before and during the transition to the use of the DSM-5, social workers sometimes referred to diagnoses that have since changed (American Psychiatric Association, 2000, 2013). The following types of disabilities are discussed by social workers in this book: psychiatric, intellectual, developmental, learning, neurological, and physical. Psychiatric disabilities included emotional, behavioral, or mental health challenges. Clients with psychiatric disabilities were often referred to as those with "ED," or emotional disabilities. Intellectual disability was previously known as mental retardation. Social workers who supported children with these disabilities often referred to them as people with "cognitive impairments" or the "sped kids," the latter denoting those who received special education services. Developmental disabilities included developmental delays, Down syndrome, and autism spectrum disorders. Learning disabilities included specific learning disorder and dyslexia. Neurological disabilities included brain injuries and dementia. Physical disabilities included any ambulatory impairments. The most common disabilities discussed by social workers were intellectual and developmental.

Choosing language to communicate about disability that is respectful and accepted universally is difficult. The U.S. disability rights movement argues for use of person-first language (that is, a person with a disability) over disability-first language (that is, a disabled person) to acknowledge that a disability is only one aspect of a person's identity (Tobin, 2011). The American Psychiatric Association has supported the disability rights movements' use of person-first language (Peers, Spencer-Cavaliere, & Eales, 2014). However, more recently, perspectives have shifted to advocating for the use of disability-first language. The social model of disability, which resulted from the U.K. disability movement, posits that people do not have disability, "but rather, societies have actively disabled people" (Peers et al., 2014, p. 273). To clarify, the societal structures have disabled (used as a verb) people. The social model of disability suggests that social structures, policies, and attitudes create disability. This model focuses on macrosystemic influences, such as societal perspectives, structures, and policies, rather than individual diagnoses. In doing so, it recognizes challenges faced by individuals as a result of living within societies that do not provide accommodations to meet their needs.

Social workers often perform their work within a medical model framework and use the DSM-5 for billing and professional communication purposes. For example, clients often need to receive a formal diagnosis to receive services; thus, reference to diagnoses becomes important in the social work profession. The social model of disability is also consistent with social work professionals who ethically strive and are bound to conduct social and political advocacy on their clients' behalf (NASW, 2015a). Social workers must balance use of the medical and social models of disability. As with any language used in social work practice, it is important to communicate with clients about their desired preference in use of disability- or person-first language. Social workers' quotes are used verbatim in line with our phenomenological perspective taken, with the exception that we removed identifying references to ensure confidentiality and made person-first language changes when it appeared disrespectful. For example, some social workers would refer to "the mentally retarded" client rather than "the client with intellectual disability." While we were writing this book, an End-the-R-Word campaign in the United States advocated for ending the use of the word "retardation." In addition, because this word was removed from the DSM-5, it seemed appropriate to make changes to represent the accurate diagnosis and use more acceptable language.

Our hope is that this book will serve as a source of information about the intimate relationships and sexual health of people with disabilities across the lifespan, including the social welfare policies and practices aimed at improving their development. We also hope that the interviewed social workers' acknowledgment of systemic challenges and ideas for radical solutions will inspire you not only to provide direct support for people with disabilities, but to advocate for changes in societal structures that have further disabled people.

2

History of Policies Restricting the Sexual Rights of People with Disabilities

People with disabilities may identify as sexual, asexual, sensual, or something else entirely. However, most media portrayals and administrative policies have treated them as asexual. *Asexuality* is defined as "a relative absence or insufficiency of sexual interest, biologically and socially described function, and interpersonal sexual engagement" (Kim, 2011, p. 481). This definition is dependent on what is considered to be sexual in the historical, social, and cultural context (Kim, 2011). Social workers in our study believe that the assumption that people with disabilities are asexual exists; they observed educators making the assumption that adolescents with disabilities cannot understand sex, let alone pursue it. Young adults with disabilities in our study also felt the stigma of asexuality. A Ghanaian American young woman with cerebral palsy expressed her feelings this way:

> The most common question I get is . . . do I feel anything down there, or really invasive questions, almost like I was subhuman . . . or I was like a science project. . . . But you do know I'm just like you, too, right? I get the same feelings or whatever that you do, so it's not weird or anything.

As stated in the first chapter, people with disabilities are as sexually active as those without. This topic will be explored throughout this book. Intimacy and sensuality are also critically important to people with disabilities and should be considered as part of a person's sexuality. Social workers described their clients' need for intimacy, such as holding hands or spending time with someone, versus engaging in physical sexual acts. Previous research on people with disabilities described sensuality as an openness to engage in pleasurable activities. Examples of sensuality might be touching skin to skin with another person or even touching the skin to soft fabrics (Kim, 2011). A social worker expressed that some of her clients are just interested in "being held, feeling closeness," such as a desire to lie next to a spouse in bed. The assumption of asexuality and ignorance surrounding the sensual and intimate needs of people with disabilities may have grown from historical policies preventing sexual expression and intimate relationships among people with disabilities (Löfgren-Mårtenson, 2013; Neuhaus, Smith, & Burgdorf, 2014).

Sexual citizenship, or a lack thereof, "relies on a series of exclusions of those who do not or cannot fit" (Shildrick, 2013, p. 138). Exclusions of sexual citizenship among people with disabilities began historically in professional practices and policies. Disability diagnoses have roots associated with sexuality, especially intellectual and psychiatric disabilities. Mental retardation was first diagnosed in 1614. The cause of the condition was documented as an "overindulgence in sexual pleasure" among the biological parents of the diagnosed individual. The diagnosis was thought to be caused by sexual activity among those who were related to one another (Kempton & Kahn, 1991; Wade, 2002). Research has supported this claim. Sexual reproduction from consanguinity, two people sharing the same blood line, has been associated with lower IQs among children (Woodley, 2009).

The reproduction of people with disabilities has been targeted and controlled throughout history. The eugenics movement (1880–1940), which sought to breed out individuals characterized as "sexual perverts" or "habitual criminals," also included people with disabilities (Wade, 2002). According to eugenicists, people with disabilities fed on society's resources and did not contribute in return. Between 1907 and 1957, approximately

60,000 people in the United States were sterilized without providing consent (Kempton & Kahn, 1991). The *Buck v. Bell* Supreme Court decision (1927) to sterilize a 17-year-old girl with an intellectual disability determined that sterilization of the "unfit," or disabled, was justifiable "for the protection and health of the state." By 1930, a total of 30 states had enacted involuntary sterilization laws (Pfeiffer, 1994; Wade, 2002). The superintendent of the Winfield Kansas State Home for the Feebleminded castrated 44 boys and 14 girls, and once the vasectomy procedure was developed, approximately 600–700 boys were sterilized at the Indiana State Reformatory (Burgdorf, 1980). The Supreme Court has never overturned *Buck v. Bell*, and sterilizations by surgery, tubal ligation, or forced birth control continue to occur, yet less frequently. In addition, half of the states passed laws declaring marriages by people deemed "insane" or "feebleminded" to be null and void; 39 states continue to prohibit marriage among people with intellectual disabilities today (Neuhaus et al., 2014). Although these laws are rarely enforced, prohibited cohabitation policies in housing services continue to be enforced (Dolak, 2013).

Until the 1960s, many people with disabilities lived in large single-sex institutions for life. The 1970s marked progress for people with disabilities. The U.S. Supreme Court decision *Wyatt v. Stickney* (1972) declared that all people with mental disorders who are involuntarily committed to mental institutions be given "with adequate supervision, suitable opportunities for the patient's interaction with members of the opposite sex." Although it clarified only allowing heterosexual relations, it acknowledged the possibility of people with disabilities to engage in intimacy. The Rehabilitation Act of 1973 (29 U.S.C. 701, et seq.) called for reasonable accommodations and prevention of discrimination for people with disabilities in employment and education. A couple years later in 1975, the Education for All Handicapped Children Act (P.L. 94-142) required that schools provide "free and appropriate public education" for all children regardless of ability.

Although the 1970s sexual revolution celebrated sexual expression among the general population, it did nothing to quell the sexual exploitation and victimization of people with disabilities. Research found that people with disabilities were at least twice as likely to experience sexual victimization as those without (Burt, 1973). These data coincided with deinstitutionalization. People with disabilities were moving into community-based housing to group homes or with families by the masses. This resulted in a fear that people with disabilities could not protect themselves in the community. Thus, policies and practices related to sexual health for people with disabilities were subsequently designed to protect them. Surveys of 82 facilities serving adults with disabilities found resistance from community members or staff to implement any policies enabling the sexual rights of their clients (Mulhern, 1975). However, it was also during this time that the NASW (1979) code of ethics specifically stated that social workers must be culturally competent in the needs of "physically handicapped" people. This was the first reference to disability in the NASW code of ethics. In addition, one facility serving people with disabilities progressively held a planning meeting with its staff to meet the sexual expression needs of clients and developed policies protecting clients' privacy related to masturbation and sexual intercourse among consenting adults, including homosexual relationships (Hall & Sawyer, 1978).

In 1990 the Americans with Disabilities Act and in 2004 IDEA were passed, which continued to protect people with disabilities from discrimination in education, employment, and public places. Although children with disabilities were more likely to be integrated into regular education classes, sex education continues not to be adapted to meet the unique needs of people with disabilities (Swango-Wilson, 2011). For example, social workers who have been working in the field since the 1990s remembered continuing to automatically terminate the parental rights of women with disabilities. It was not until 2001 that the CSWE Educational Policy and Accreditation Standards mandated that disability-related curricula be included in social work education (CSWE, 2001). In that same year, the NASW code of ethics broadened the scope of disability and mandated that social workers be culturally competent in the needs of people with "mental and physical disabilities" (NASW, 2001).

In contrast to the eugenics movement, which aimed to improve human genetic traits through reduced rates of reproduction and sterilization among people with societally undesired characteristics, a new technology movement is developing bionic limbs or body parts to improve the lives of people with and without disabilities. Bionic limbs are prosthetics that are controlled by a person's mind and have the ability of senses, such as sight or touch, unlike previous prosthetics. For example, a blind man who received bionic eyes was able to see his wife for the first time in over a decade (Yam, 2015). This technology has become so popular that people without disabilities are interested in using it for body replacement purposes or as add-ons to enhance their physical abilities (Panesar & Wolbring, 2014). With three-dimensional (3-D) printing, bionic limbs are becoming affordable to the general population. With popularity among people with and without disabilities and the new accessibility with 3-D printing, this technology movement is demonstrating how changes in society, such as the availability of technologies, may offer choices regarding disability. These ideas are not without controversy but certainly could have implications for intimate relationships and dating among people with and without disabilities. If these technologies continue to develop and were to become easily accessible and affordable, one could potentially choose whether to have at least certain types of disability. However, as social workers, we understand that it is often those most in need of services that have the largest financial, social, and situational barriers to achieving them. Furthermore, like other aspects of diversity, disability is often a central point of identity and a source of pride (Ballan, 2008). Thus, conversations concerning the intersection of new technologies and disability will need to be considered carefully from a strengths perspective that meets clients in their understanding of disability within their environment.

THEORIES

Two prominent theories that have critiqued the historical treatment of intimate and sexual health needs of people with disabilities are the social model of disability and crip theory. The social model of disability posits that people are only as disabled as the social and physical environment make them; that is, disability is the result of societally stigmatizing environments that are nonaccessible and nonaccommodating to an individual. Impairments, which are functional limitations caused by physical, mental, or sensory challenges, are distinguished from disability, which is the loss or limitation of life opportunities on an equal level to others (Oliver, 1990, 1996). The social model of disability argues that "nothing about disabled people is wrong and needs to be fixed" (Anastasiou & Kauffman, 2013, p. 443). Supports for people with impairments should focus on society's social and physical structures that enhance the inclusion of all people in life opportunities; for example, gynecology offices should offer pamphlets in braille so as not to exclude blind individuals from important sexual health information (Ballan, 2008). This model recognizes that societies and responses to individuals within them have been developed from "norms" that, in effect, often serve to exclude people with impairments and create obstacles to their healthy sexual expression and sexual citizenship (see Ballan, 2008). Crip theory critiques the concept of normativity related to ableism and heterosexuality. Crip is short for "cripple" and is intended to be provocative. The theorist Robert McRuer (2006) embodied pride in disability and being crippled. Although the theory started by referring only to physical ability and disability, it now includes people with various disabilities. Similar to the social model of disability, crip theory posits that impairment exists only as a contrast to able-bodiedness (Löfgren-Mårtenson, 2013). Crip theory has specifically criticized practices and policies related to sexuality of people with disabilities. It argues that surgical sterilization to prevent procreation among people with disabilities was a significant measure to "distinguish the sexuality of the disabled from the 'normates'" (Löfgren-Mårtenson, 2013, p. 416). Both theories emphasize the importance of assessing how societal structures hinder or embrace intimacy and sexual expression of people with disabilities.

The following chapters in this book describe current social work practices and responses to the sexual, sensual, and intimate health needs of people with disabilities. There are tensions in social services; there is an acknowledgment that people with disabilities are engaging in sex or other forms of sexuality, sensuality, or intimacy, yet very little attention is paid to reproductive health care needs and education. School social workers are often employed in abstinence-only school districts, yet are posed with questions by their clients that are better answered with comprehensive sexual education. Some policies even prescribe punitive measures in response to people with disabilities expressing their sexuality in hopes of protecting them from being sexually exploited (Wright, McCabe, & Kooreman, 2012). Conversely, sexual surrogacy is taking place. In this practice, professionals and nonprofessionals conduct talk therapy and practice sensual and sexual behaviors with people with disabilities who are either inexperienced sexually or cannot find a partner with whom to comfortably and safely express their needs (Leyson, 2013). Social workers have an ethical dilemma. According to the NASW (2015a) code of ethics, it is their ethical responsibility to promote the well-being of their clients, including preventing them from being victims of sex crimes and providing related sexual health education, yet social workers also must promote client self-determination and assist in their goals related to developing intimate and sexual relationships.

IMPLICATIONS FOR SOCIAL WORK PRACTICE

The historical practices and policies preventing intimacy and sexuality do not remain in the past. The *Buck v. Bell* Supreme Court decision (1927), in which sterilization of people with disabilities was determined justifiable, has not been overturned. States continue to prohibit marriage of people with intellectual disabilities (Neuhaus et al., 2014). Use of forced birth control continues to exist. Adults with disabilities whose children were automatically removed from them may continue to mourn the loss of raising their children (Neuhaus et al., 2014). From the standpoint of a social model of disability, policies and practices should be forged in such a manner that allows full sexual citizenship for all peoples, including those with physical, mental, or sensory limitations (Oliver, 1996). Social workers of today should live out the position of the social model of disability. Social workers should empower individuals with disabilities by calling attention to and changing the social structures that have limited the sexual expression of people with disabilities in the past and that continue to do so now.

3

Healthy Sexuality Begins in Childhood

A life course perspective recognizes that sexuality begins in childhood and that relationships are important to the individual regardless of age (NASW, 2015a). A broad definition of sexuality recognizes it as integral to humanity. Concepts such as the need for intimate connection and relationships, the importance of self-esteem, socialization, privacy, and safety, as well as physical maturation, hygiene, and knowledge of one's own and others' bodies are used to describe sexuality (Murphy et al., 2006; Parchomiuk, 2012; Taylor Gomez, 2012). It is important that social workers recognize sexuality as a facet of childhood development. In the following sections, we will discuss micro-, meso-, exo-, and macrosystemic factors that were salient in our interviews with social workers serving children with a range of disabilities. *Children* are defined as being between the ages of three and 11, given that around age three is when many children are entering preschool and age 11 marks the end of the middle childhood years (Centers for Disease Control and Prevention, 2015).

As part of developing sexuality, people learn relationship skills beginning in early childhood (Murphy et al., 2006); however, children with a range of disabilities often face societal and individual challenges to developing positive social relationships and self-esteem (O'Toole & Doe, 2002) and may need additional support to learn how to have safe and healthy relationships to maximize eventual romantic relationship and sexual potential. This chapter describes factors unique to relationship and sexual development of children with disabilities, including self-esteem, socialization, maturation, gender identity development, victimization and safety, and barriers to receiving professional support.

MICROSYSTEM
Individual: Self-Esteem

During childhood, individuals begin to understand themselves as part of a social world. They receive verbal and nonverbal feedback from peers and other members of their social circles and, through interpretation of this information, develop a sense of self-worth and confidence. Social workers in our study describe numerous challenges to the formation of healthy self-concept and self-esteem among children with disabilities; some relate directly to disability-related impairments, whereas others relate to bullying, exclusion, or victimization by peers. Sometimes difficulty in one area would contribute to a poor sense of self in another. Children with disabilities, like typical youths (Fattore, Mason, & Watson, 2009), often recognize the value placed on education as it relates to their long-term quality of life and ability to form meaningful goals. They are also increasingly able to form social comparisons where they may recognize that they fall behind peers (Foley et al., 2012). We find in our study that social exclusion due to special education leads to ridicule from other children in the child's microsystem, resulting in a second belief that he or she is also socially incompetent. This belief is supported by the way the educational system is set up with "special" attention for children with disabilities, as the following social worker describes. The latter part of this quote describes behaviors typical of children with learning or mental health disorders who struggled with classroom tasks:

> Dignity is a big one because . . . I mean, you failed because you can't be in your regular classroom on your regular campus . . . and then

you come to a special school. . . . Yes, there are dignity issues, but that's kind of like how the school system is set up. . . . All the kids in your neighborhood see the special bus coming for you. . . . There's something wrong with you and [there is] not. It's just that you need a little bit more support. . . . If you need a place to yell or scream and then come back to class, you have that and somebody here to help you work through those things.

This social worker elaborates on how sexual behaviors specifically can ostracize a child in a system that is unaccepting and sees disability as the problem:

Could you imagine being the kid on the campus going after the teacher's breasts and trying to bite the teacher's breasts and saying all kinds of things to the teacher? Well, yeah, because all the kids are going to talk about you.

Sexual behaviors specifically include demonstrating interest in one's own or another person's sex, looking at another individual in the nude, touching genitals, and wanting to be close in proximity to other people; the extent to which these behaviors are considered developmentally normal vary by gender and age (see Kellogg, 2010, for age-appropriate sexual behaviors in children). It is not uncommon for children with or without disabilities as early as age two to become interested in touching genitals or breasts (Kellogg, 2010), although some children with disabilities may have difficulty expressing sexual thoughts and feelings in a socially acceptable manner (see McLay, Carnett, Tyler-Merrick, & van deer Meer, 2015, for a review). Social workers should familiarize themselves with normative versus atypical sexual behaviors in children and adolescents, as well as be familiar with how disability and sociocultural factors may intersect within each individual child's ecosystem. Sensory needs may be particularly relevant to certain disabilities (Nichols & Blakeley-Smith, 2010), leading youths with autism spectrum disorders, for example, to act impulsively without accurate assessment of the external contexts and to display more sexually expressive behaviors, often deemed "inappropriate" (Ballan, 2012; Ray, Marks, & Bray-Garretson, 2004; Stokes & Kaur, 2005). The social model of disability recognizes the failure of educational and community systems in accommodating the unique needs and experiences of each child. This model recognizes the special gifts, talents, and attributes of each child; where it pertains to education more broadly, it strays from a "one size fits all" set of educational standards. As this applies to our discussion of relationship (for example, peers, family) and sexual health (for example, person as sexual, boundaries), Barnard-Brak, Schmidt, Chesnut, Wei, and Richman (2014) discuss how education may need to be tailored to individuals with a disability to ensure that content is understood and acceptable to the child and family and is consistent with mandates set forth by IDEA (2004). For the child to develop a strong sense of self, it is essential to promote positive and inclusive attitudes about disability within a life course approach that centralizes the importance of relationships with other peers and adults.

As social workers, we learn to assess children's appraisals of themselves as part of biopsychosocial-spiritual assessments. Children with disabilities are often affected by medications or by the disability itself, and this can cause self-esteem challenges as a child begins to compare him- or herself to other peers. One social worker reflects on how girls with Down syndrome often have more awareness than others about how they look different than their peers and desire to look like everyone else. Another social worker describes working with children who had transplant surgeries that stunted their growth and who subsequently struggle with self-esteem. Foley and colleagues (2012) found in their focus groups with children with a range of disabilities (that is, autism spectrum disorders, cerebral palsy, Down syndrome, vision impairment) that these youths struggled with body image. We similarly find that social workers support children and youths with eating disorders who cope with emotional pain. Although many of the children suffer from poor self-esteem, some also exhibit resiliency in the face of challenges related to their disability. Often these stories entail an embracing of disability-related differences:

> We have one girl who's had that rare disorder and lost her hair. . . . It never grew back. . . . I'm sure people have made fun of her . . . but she has this amazing resiliency that she could really care less. . . . She has a wig, but she prefers not to wear it.

Finally, a child's developing sense of sexual orientation and gender identity is an important facet of sexuality (Kellogg, 2010). Children learn to identify as a specific sex and "do" gender (that is, express various gendered behaviors as culturally influenced) from a very young age. The ability to safely and comfortably express these behaviors is part of a child's self-esteem development (Christensen, Wright, & Dunn, 2016), and some of the social workers in our study discuss how parents come to them after their child asks questions about gender identity or exhibits gendered behaviors that stray from cultural norms:

> It's becoming more common that parents are actually seeking out treatment and therapy for their kids by the ages four, five, and six who are saying things early on about . . . "I'm not a boy" or "I'm not a girl," or . . . actually claiming to their parents that they are the opposite sex, and you know showing signs very early on of wanting to dress like the opposite gender, you know wanting to, or even being attracted to somebody of the same gender.

Social workers should be aware that some parents might react to a child's questioning or behaviors with distress, which may create feelings of shame. Sexualization is culturally, including religiously, influenced (Kellogg, 2010). Social workers should take care to assess their own feelings with regard to sexuality and sexual orientation and their ability to help parents to respond to a child's sexual questioning and behaviors with acceptance, curiosity, and an attitude of exploration. Social workers in our study play a number of important roles with regard to building sexual-esteem, including equipping themselves with a strong knowledge base concerning specialized referrals. One social worker describes locating an expert therapist for gender identity support. With regard to body image, social workers can also help youths to build a sense of resilience by helping children to recognize and counter popularized peer and media messages that overemphasize physical attractiveness, often failing to represent various body types (Foley et al., 2012). Children with disabilities state that positive self-image is enhanced by goal setting, personal achievement, and not wanting to be underestimated in what they can accomplish (Foley et al., 2012); a strengths perspective should be kept at the forefront when thinking about sexual and relationship health.

Peer: Challenges and Resiliencies

Self-esteem is enhanced when children have opportunities for prosocial involvement. Foley and colleagues (2012) found that children with disabilities identified a sense of belonging, reinforced through shared activities and close friends, as the most important component for having a good life. Children stated that they turned to their close friends for advice and as sources of support. Other research has similarly found that youths turn to their friends for information related to relationships and sexuality (Adams & Williams, 2011a). Getting teased about their disability served as a barrier to experiencing well-being (Foley et al., 2012).

Many social workers in our study describe forging strong peer relationships as the most fundamental challenge of children with a wide range of disabilities and levels of severity, mirroring research in this area (De Boer, Pijl, Post, & Minnaert, 2013). Social workers receive advanced training in human development within social environments partially to understand how normative development may deviate from atypical development. Thus, social workers are often able to identify children as having one or more disabilities and to prioritize the importance of their relationships with peers, which is consistent with the NASW (2015a) code of ethics. Social workers individualize their approach to each child within a strengths framework that capitalizes on the developmental need for intimacy and peer acceptance. Furthermore, they work within societal notions of acceptability for various sexualized behaviors. For example, children with autism spectrum disorder sometimes engage in sexual behaviors, such as masturbating, in a public school setting. Another social worker serving primarily youths with autism spectrum disorder and intellectual disability describes a child who struggled with peer boundaries:

> He was an individual who actually has always been kind of more affectionate, and who has you know always liked being close to people and being hugged constantly. . . . As he kind of grew up and . . . reached puberty, we started to realize . . . those things that might be appropriate for him to do when he's a younger child are now not appropriate anymore . . . that it's not appropriate for him to, you know, hug and kiss strangers and want to sit in people's laps that he doesn't know.

Social workers discuss negotiating appropriate settings for sexual behaviors and physical boundaries for affection sharing as common challenges for children with disabilities. Similarly, they describe the importance of working with children with disabilities to improve their social skills. This lack of skills often stems from an inability to negotiate complex sensory or social environments. Like typically developing children, children with disabilities are learning to regulate emotions as a central task of their development (Ashford & LeCroy, 2013) and may face challenges related to their disability (see Ballan, 2012). Some genetic conditions as well as other developmental disabilities (for example, Down, Prader–Willi, and Williams syndromes) may result in inappropriate sexual behaviors, self-injury, social skills deficits, emotional outbursts, and impulsivity (Watson, Richards, Miodrag, & Fedoroff, 2012). They may also include advanced or delayed bodily changes as a result of biomedical issues that affect sexual timing and functioning, all of which can change how a child is viewed by their peers (Watson et al., 2012). Some children prefer not to interact with other kids, sometimes withdraw from their peers, and would rather play games alone.

Social isolation, lashing out, or difficulty making sense of social cues can lead other kids to pick on children with disabilities. Social workers in our study describe children struggling with hygiene as associated with depression or resistance to personal daily living tasks. This is supported by other research (Nichols & Blakeley-Smith, 2010; Stokes & Kaur, 2005; Swango-Wilson, 2009). Teasing by peers often contributes to a negative feedback loop in which self-esteem is further hindered and poor emotional regulation adds even more strain to relationships:

> There's a lot of kids [with disabilities] with a lot of yelling and screaming and profanity. A lot of it is just their self-esteem is low and they mask. Whereas somebody on the outside may see it as, "Oh, that's just an angry child." Well, no.

Often social workers believe that children who lack self-esteem and are victimized by their peers become bullies themselves.

Children with certain types of disabilities may have an easier time forming peer relationships. Social workers observe that kids with visible disabilities sometimes are able to form better relationships than those with invisible disabilities:

> Well, you know, with children with physical handicaps, oftentimes those children in school have good peer relationships. Because number one, the other kids want to help them. I'll never forget . . . there was a child with Down syndrome. And she was fairly low functioning, but everybody in that school knew that kid, and they loved her.

In contrast, the same social worker notes that kids did not respond the same way to children with emotional disabilities, because they did not understand their behaviors:

> So, you know, different disabilities bring different things. And, of course, kids with . . . emotional problems, they . . . have fits. Like this one girl I see. And she's in the fifth grade, and she was under the desk for an hour yesterday at school. So those are the kind of things that put kids off terribly.

Similarly, a study of Dutch students' attitudes found that more positive attitudes were held for others who were blind, deaf, or paralyzed than those who were intellectually disabled (De Laat, Freriksen, & Vervloed, 2013). However, the intersections of disability type, level of severity, and peer relationships were complex. This is similar to what we find with the social workers in our study. For example, although visible disabilities sometimes elicit feelings of empathy and care from peers, at other times peers fear or feel uncomfortable around children with physical impairments. Children with disabilities also respond in various ways, at times directly owning the disability to prevent or counter other children's negative reactions. This social worker describes a five-year-old with extensive burns all over her body as a result of being left in the closet with her brother when her house burned down:

> She actually used that difference as an advantage. There was a little boy that was very scared of her because of [her burns], and so when they would go out and play on the playground, and she wanted to use the swing and he was using it, she would go over and spook him to use that.

Similarly, this social worker says she had a client with cerebral palsy who has one arm that remains next to her body and who walks with a limp, but she was "probably the toughest little girl in her classroom, and I think she's developed that toughness. It's almost, like, don't you dare ask me about my arm." Social workers' roles include helping children to understand why other kids might be reacting with fear, judgment, or bullying and to interrupt the cycle so that children do not become aggressors themselves:

> I feel we end up . . . focusing even more on those children to build even additional skills and additional abilities to deal with those reactions and those responses. "He doesn't want to play with me? Why do you think?" And so, having those conversations openly with the kids about what their disability may mean to others.

Thus, if there is one thing to remember about children with disabilities and social workers' roles in helping them to forge healthy sexual identities, it is the importance of peer relationships. This social worker describes the issues that children on her caseload typically encounter:

> What they talk about is, like, at lunch they don't have anyone to play with . . . and they don't get invited to birthday parties and they don't get invited to sleepovers and seldom do they get to go to somebody's house to play or invite someone to their house to play.

Social workers should strive to build opportunities for children with disabilities to have positive peer interactions by working within the child's micro-, meso-, and macrosystems to help others recognize disability as an aspect of diversity. Children learn to form positive attitudes and form friendships with differently abled peers by spending quality time together (De Laat et al., 2013). Still, as discussed by the social workers in our study, this area presents a particularly challenging area of practice. Bullying and victimization are such prevalent problems, and children with disabilities are at a higher risk to experience persecution and violence than other children (Jones et al., 2012). Thus, teaching children to recognize when they are being victimized and how to report it to a parent or other adult they can trust to help them is important: "a lot of realizing when you're being bullied and when you need to stand up for yourself and what you need to do."

MESOSYSTEM

Parents and Caregivers: Strengths and Barriers

Children with disabilities discuss family life as being an important component of their well-being. Homes marked by parental warmth and sibling support offer youths an opportunity to form healthy relationships, whereas situations of divorce, lack of safety, and other home stressors act as barriers to positive life experiences (Foley et al., 2012). Forging meaningful relationships is a way for youths to build resilience and contributes positively to their developing sexuality. Social workers in our study also describe parents as sources of strength and resilience. They shared information with social workers concerning what their child did not receive or understand from sexual health classes in school, took their child to social events to build their social skills, and implemented sexual and relationship health tools learned from their social work practitioner and in the home context.

Children with disabilities may benefit from relationship closeness in the home as experienced amid collectivist cultures. This social worker describes her work with Hispanic youths:

> Their culture really embraces family and togetherness and, you know, connectivity and spending time together. For families who were very warm and loving and always greet each other with a hug and a smile and a kiss, you know, I think that can send some really positive messages.

The social worker should aim to build rapport with families, prioritizing the family's most pressing needs and educating about the interconnectedness of sexual and relationship health as normative and important aspects of development. Connecting parents to support groups in the community not only provides opportunities for children with similar challenges to form friendships but also offers caregivers respite and emotional support.

Perhaps because of some of the barriers discussed, social workers in our study often view parents and caregivers as challenges to promoting the sexual and relationship health of children with disabilities. At times parents lack acceptance of their child's disability or of needed services or education, overprotect their child, or struggle themselves with one or more disabilities. Sometimes well-meaning parents can overprotect their children out of fear of victimization (McKenzie & Swartz, 2011). A young Mexican American man with dyslexia and attention deficit/hyperactivity disorder reflects on his overprotective parents:

> My parents are really helicopter parents, so they're always hovering over me. I couldn't go out. I couldn't really do stuff outside the house. I had to be around the house all the time. I would try to get out and do stuff around my neighborhood, which was play basketball, or just talk to the neighbor friends, the kids my age.

In Ballan's (2012) study with parents of children with autism spectrum disorder (ages six through 13 years), parents wanted additional information from health care professionals on how to prevent sexual victimization, including their own ability to detect abuse, and on how to improve their child's ability to report it. Social workers in our study most often describe fear of emotional victimization in the form of bullying:

> As kids continue to get a little bit older when you would expect them to have more freedom and independence, like, they're capable of going out with friends unsupervised or . . . going to a movie . . . or being able to spend the night at someone's house, going to parties with friends, their parents tend to be . . . understandably so—more protective, more concerned that their child could be teased or made fun of, that they might end up in a situation that they don't know how to handle.

This overprotection, however, could increase a child's vulnerability through a lack of opportunities to build self-esteem and to learn socialization skills (McKenzie & Swartz, 2011). This separation from other children can also lead to a lack of knowledge surrounding relationships and sexuality. Furthermore, parents' views on sexuality influence their acceptance of and reaction to their children's developing sexual selves and the extent to which they view sexual behaviors as normative versus disruptive or abnormal. Education, culture, and family stressors influence parents' viewpoints (Kellogg, 2010). Challenges surrounding individual and peer relationships of children with disabilities, as well as the emergence of sexual behaviors, often alarm parents and caregivers. Social workers can help parents, caregivers, and family members to better understand what the child may be experiencing and educate them concerning the importance of opportunities for prosocial involvement that include outlets for affection sharing and receiving.

As discussed, an ecological approach to supporting children with disabilities in developing healthy intimate and sexual development that includes attention to family, peer, and community is recommended (see Larkin, Felitti, & Anda, 2014). In addition to maximizing strengths within the family and caregiver system, the social worker works across ecological systems to advocate for greater attention to the ways in which society has ostracized, ignored, oppressed, or "othered" children with disabilities. Paradoxically, the social worker must aim to work within existing systems to maximize effective resource provision and meet the family's needs concerning the developing sexual and relationship health of the child. In practice, this may mean that a child's sexual behaviors may be reframed for a family as normative, "acceptable" within cultural and societal definitions, and existing within a framework that prioritizes the child's need for self-expression, positive body image, and self-esteem. Furthermore, many social workers in our study express that parents held limited views of their child's potential for later dating or romantic and sexual relationships. Studies are needed to longitudinally assess how these attitudes affect children's developing sense of self as relational and sexual beings, but we do know from research (and as later discussed in the following chapters) that adolescents and adults with disabilities are desiring of these types of meaningful intimate relationships. The information in the following chapters should be shared with parents of children with disabilities, highlighting the importance of a life course and strengths-based approach to sexual and relationship health.

Raising a child with a disability can be stressful, and sometimes grandparents (Larkin et al., 2014) or siblings (Hartling et al., 2014) may also be involved. It is important to remember that the family's emotional and instrumental resources are often taxed. A social worker details the many challenges these children face, some of which intersect with trauma to include attachment problems, substance abuse, attention deficit/hyperactivity disorder, mood disorders, and schizophrenia. The social worker observes, "The parents are depressed and angry and pulling their hair out." Cindy Liu, disability advocate and a mother of a young daughter with Down syndrome, describes the stress of raising a child with a disability as "disability fatigue." She attributes this fatigue to the day-to-day caregiving responsibilities as well as fighting inequality related to disability (Liu, 2017).

In assessing the family system, social workers serving children with disabilities describe siblings as sometimes beneficial to the child's developing relational self, specifically when they form meaningful and protective relationships. Although fighting or arguing with siblings is typical of any youth, this, however, posed additional challenges for children with disabilities. Furthermore, social workers note that it is important they assess potential for victimization or perpetrating behaviors on behalf of siblings, including the child with a disability (that is, as abuser or victim), when family or child functioning indicates risk.

Social workers in our study discuss the importance of consistency and positive parenting in the development of a child's sexual and relational health. They sometimes came to serve youths through foster care, child protective, or juvenile justice contexts. It is common that children with disabilities also experience trauma, which intersects with disability in complex ways. The following quote captures an overemphasis on the medical model in social work, where sexuality is more openly discussed in problematic contexts. This may be compared with a general apprehension among health care providers, parents, and society to proactively discuss positive aspects of sexuality with children (Christensen et al., 2016).

> Two years ago I did more traditional social work with families who had adopted through the state. . . . So they had been abused and neglected and removed from their birth families, gone into the foster system, and then adopted into new families. Those kids did a lot of sexual acting out, mostly because they were sexually abused or they . . . had seen sexual stuff going on . . . so that population I mean . . . sexual behavior is much more discussed.

Many youths had been sexually assaulted, often by a family member. In a study of over 40,000 forensic abuse statements, children with disabilities were more likely to have been sexually abused than typically developing youths. They were also more likely to be abused by a parent or guardian and to have delayed reporting the suspected abuse. They were also more likely to have experienced repeated offenses, bodily injury, threats, and use of force. Risk was associated with severity of disability (Hershkowitz, Lamb, & Horowitz, 2007). Some social workers in our study consider trauma a disability in and of itself. This is consistent with recent movements to include developmental trauma within the DSM-5 (van der Kolk et al., 2009; as cited by Bremness & Polzin, 2014):

> That you see some kids really crave and want this [affection], but then aren't even sure, you know, what to do with it once they have it. . . . I think of kids probably exposed more to trauma that have such a difficult time because . . . sometimes the person that is taking care of you is the same person that is kind of hurting you, and so . . . that affection might be the prelude to some real harm.

In addition to having experienced sexual assault, many other children with disabilities come from homes affected by domestic violence, neglect, or other forms of trauma. Social workers need to understand the higher incidence of abuse and trauma among children with disabilities and their tendency to not disclose this abuse (Hershkowitz et al., 2007). Most often, abuse will have been or is being perpetrated by someone within the child's daily routine (that is, school, day care, or home environment; Baladerian, Coleman, & Stream, 2013).

Social Workers

A collaborative approach to care is extremely important in working to promote the sexual and relationship health of children with disabilities. We find that social workers often support mesosystemic functioning by facilitating communication about a child's developing sexuality and relationships among professionals, family, school, and community agencies, such as parents and special education. Social workers refer children to

Big Brothers/Big Sisters, to community mentors, and to other families for social support. Social workers also refer families to community resources for mental health support and to school or community-based counseling services. This includes support for building self-esteem and self-advocacy skills, as well as specialized referrals. Brokering to services for sexuality support includes helping to find same-gender helping professionals to support maturation issues within a school setting. Finally, social workers also conduct referrals for individual and family counseling, case management, and rape crisis.

Some social workers do not feel it is their place to discuss issues of sexuality, although social skills and relationship building are more within their comfort zones. These social workers in our study defer sexuality to others within the child's microsystem, such as their parents. Others feel that they are not equipped to handle sexuality concerns, especially as these intersect with disability. This is consistent with the NASW (2015a) code of ethics principle stating that social workers should practice within areas of their competence. For example, one social worker we met indicated that he relied on a specialist working with the child, an applied behavior analysis therapist. Another social worker referred a parent to the child's doctor for sexual maturation questions about her son with physical disabilities. When social workers are approached by parents and other professionals about issues concerning sexuality, how to handle bodily changes is a common theme: "She [mom] would be like, he's getting bigger and he's getting older, do kids with autism—do they have the same feelings as other children?"

Research has found that both health care professionals and educators occasionally feel unprepared to address sexuality education, at times overlooking or deferring those responsibilities (East & Orchard, 2014; Fader Wilkenfeld & Ballan, 2011). A Ghanaian American young woman with cerebral palsy reflects on a teacher interfering in her development of an innocent relationship with a boy at her preschool:

> He would try to hold my hand while I was still holding onto my walker. I always thought it was cute. Our teacher was like, "You're gonna make her fall. Don't do that." I always just thought that she

had a problem with it, maybe because we had a disability or maybe because we were young. I'll never know. It would take him a long time to do it again, because he would always be afraid that she would say something.

Parents desire more professional support concerning the sexual development of their children with disabilities, including how to assess readiness, how to keep their children safe (Pownall, Jahoda, & Hastings, 2012), what to expect, and how to manage potential challenges or obstacles (Ballan, 2012), as do people with disabilities themselves (Nguyen, Liamputtong, & Monfries, 2016; Swango-Wilson, 2009, 2010). Kellogg (2010) recommends that health care practitioners be equipped to understand sexual behavior across the developmental spectrum, conduct biopsychosocial assessments that include a sexual behavior component, report suspected abuse, and work with parents to normalize sexual behavior. Foley and colleagues (2012) also recommend that helping professionals' roles in serving children with disabilities include fostering opportunities for meaningful relationships with friends and family members, recognizing and helping youths to cope with stressors (for example, school, bullying), promoting positive self-image to include body image, and educating the community about how to adjust the environment and discourse to benefit all types of individuals.

EXOSYSTEM AND MACROSYSTEM

Exo- and macrosystemic challenges prevent children with disabilities from developing healthy sexual identities and relationships with others. School provides an opportunity for socialization among both typically developing kids and those with disabilities; however, most bullying also occurs in school settings (Baladerian et al., 2013). Regardless of inclusive versus separate schooling settings, social workers describe how school climates that ostracize and label children with disabilities as less capable hinder opportunities for positive socialization. Moreover, children with disabilities are commonly not accepted to regular day care, recreation programs, or summer camps. In this way, macrosystemic attitudes about disability foster exosystemic challenges in the formation of environmental regulations. Such regulations create additional social, emotional, and financial burdens on the microsystem:

> Let's get him into day care. Let's get him into a rec program so he can work with other kids. Well, nobody wants him. There's nothing. There's nothing for if you have a severe behavior [issue], so then you'll leave them at home again. . . . Then you stop working so that you can stay at home with him and then you have no—so it's like a Catch-22.

Purposeful attention is needed to foster attitudes that view disability as an aspect of diversity (NASW, 2015a) and to create resources that help families with children with disabilities to meet their needs and to promote the child's opportunities for positive socialization. This includes raising "typical" children to be inclusive and empathic and to appreciate children who are different from them. Furthermore, sexuality should be directly addressed and promoted in a positive way, rather than responded to negatively or narrowed to prevention or intervention (Winges-Yanez, 2014). However, failure to talk about sexuality reflects a larger societal discomfort. As this social worker explains, keeping discussion of disability and sexuality from public discourse keeps progress from happening at their intersection:

> If you're embarrassed to talk to your [typical] 10-year-old about sex, then I think you're probably going to be even more embarrassed to talk to your child with a disability. . . . I think in some ways, there's a parallel between society talking about sex and society talking about disabilities. That we're not—we're not very open about talking about disabilities, and in the same way, we're not very open about talking about sexuality.

Some social workers in our study also observe that certain cultures are less open to dialogue concerning sexuality, particularly Hispanic and African American clientele (common ethnicities of the areas we sampled). It is interesting to note that the same hesitancy evidenced in the above quote was also apparent for a different social worker who feels that disability itself is seldom discussed among Hispanic and African American cultures. This social worker and others explain that certain clients may have difficulty accepting that their child has a disability, particularly after all that they had endured (for example, immigration) to obtain the life they had envisioned for their child. Consistent with research (see Sabina, Cuevas, & Schally, 2012), social workers voice that Hispanic families may be less likely to seek help from formal helping professionals. It is likely that help seeking for sexuality- and socialization-related concerns is negatively affected by language barriers, low levels of acculturation, and foreign immigration status (Sabina et al., 2012). One social worker mentions that sexual health is a taboo topic and not discussed at all among a Vietnamese family on his caseload. Finally, culture also intersects with religious viewpoints. Hispanic clients often come from a strong Catholic tradition (Organista, 2007), and some of the areas surveyed were also conservative. Some social workers' clients hold viewpoints that sexuality should not be discussed with the child. Seeking to understand the beliefs, values, and religious and cultural traditions of their families is an important aspect of promoting the sexual and relationship health of children with disabilities.

In addition to culturally influenced belief systems that affect their work, many social workers discuss political barriers to meeting the service-related needs of children with disabilities. These challenges are exacerbated for children from immigrant families who are often not eligible for needed programs:

> I would say probably the biggest challenge and the most frustrating challenge is trying to find services for those children who are not American citizens, because you see them struggling, you know they need help. You know they need the medical attention, or the medication, or whatever the case may be—but because they're not U.S. citizens, they are not eligible for a lot of the community programs or a lot of the state-funded programs. And so it's frustrating and . . . it's very time-consuming to find nonprofits and other programs that can work with special needs children who are undocumented.

The field of social work comes from a long history of advocating for equality for all, which includes educating the public on the consequences of injustices (NASW, 2015b). As we have learned in this chapter, children with disabilities face a number of unique challenges to their sexual and relationship health that require special knowledge and vocal advocating at various levels of the ecosystem. More education is needed in schools of social work concerning how practitioners can better advocate for the sexual and relationship health needs of people with disabilities by taking a life course approach that begins in childhood. Chapter 5 is dedicated specifically to sexual health education for people with disabilities of all ages, with special attention to youths.

IMPLICATIONS FOR SOCIAL WORK PRACTICE

As discussed, childhood is a critical time for the formation of sexuality, including fostering strong relationships with important people in a child's microsystem. Social workers face challenges to supporting the dignity, success, and worth of a child with disabilities. These children are often considered asexual, isolated from sexual health information, and assumed to be incapable of forming romantic and sexual relationships later in life. These societal messages affect policies and practices. At the heart of social work is the valuing of human relationships (NASW, 2015a) and the human dignity of all individuals. Direct practice implications for social workers include working to foster self-esteem, peer relationships, and sexual health, including knowledge of healthy relationships and safety, sexual anatomy, hygiene practices, maturation, and gender identity development.

Social workers in our study focus their practice examples predominantly on the ways that they work with children with disabilities to foster self-esteem and peer relationships. One social worker asks her clients to write down something good about themselves on sticky notes. To facilitate peer relationship building among children with disabilities, it is important to teach children appropriate boundaries. One social worker provides an example of a child who was struggling with appropriate physical boundaries, such as wanting to hug people he just met:

> Teach him that if you want to get somebody's attention or, you know, want to say hi to someone, this is how you introduce yourself, this is

how you shake their hand, you know, this is how you ask them a question . . . versus going up and grabbing somebody or hugging them.

Social workers support children with disabilities who are at times the bully. It is important that social workers understand the higher prevalence of bullying among children with disabilities and teach youths to identify, report, and cope with bullying (Foley et al., 2012). They should also recognize the greater vulnerability for a child with a disability to experience multiple forms of victimization, including sexual victimization (Jones et al., 2012). Social workers should work with kids to recognize abuse and know how to talk to a trusted adult about it. Social workers will need to collect a detailed biopsychosocial assessment (Kellogg, 2010). They should be prepared to make a report to child protective services in the case that abuse may be taking place (Kellogg, 2010).

CONCLUSION

Children are highly influenced by meso-, exo-, and macrosystems. Social workers often work with parents and other professionals in a child's mesosystem to obtain needed resources and services (Rueda, Bolin, Linton, Williams, & Pesta, 2016), and macro-level changes are required so that services are provided to families in need. Social workers can (a) educate children, their families, and other professionals about sexuality as a regular and healthy part of the human experience, inclusive of all people, and beginning in childhood; and (b) rely on inclusive learning environments (in which children with and without disabilities learn alongside one another) to foster acceptance of difference in social and sexual expression among children with and without disabilities.

4

Romantic Relationships, Intimacy, and Sexuality

Starting in adolescence and continuing into adulthood, the desire for a romantic relationship is both developmentally appropriate and expected. Romantic relationships are mutually acknowledged by those involved, and an intimate bond is developed through the sharing of personal thoughts, feelings, and companionable interactions. Romantic commitment emerges after these intimate and passionate moments are established and sustained (Connolly & McIsaac, 2011). Adolescents and adults have similar ideas on what romantic love means (that is, intimacy, passion, and commitment; Sternberg, 1986; Williams & Hickle, 2010). Unlike adults, however, adolescents are faced with two competing developmental needs: a desire for intimacy within the context of a close romantic relationship and a desire to engage in identity exploration by trying on different roles (Montgomery, 2005). These two goals are manifested in romantic relationships in two distinct ways: the search for an exclusive, committed, and emotionally involved relationship (a form of intimacy) and the search for a nonexclusive, low-commitment, and less emotionally intense relationship (exploration). The conflicting and competing nature of these goals can be understood within a developmental lens. Adolescents often want to experience love in an intimate and close romantic relationship but at the same time have difficulty remaining committed to the same person.

National data indicate that most adolescents will have more than one romantic relationship during their teenage years; four relationships are the mode (Connolly & McIsaac, 2009b). The longevity of romantic relationships increases with age. For example, adolescents under 14 years of age rarely are in a romantic relationship for longer than four months (Carver, Joyner, & Udry, 2003), 16-year-old relationships typically last six months, and 18-year-old relationships often endure for a year or more (Connolly & Johnson, 1996). The other side of this is that adolescents' likelihood of experiencing a breakup increases with age as well. Just under half of early adolescents have experienced a breakup, and this approaches almost 100 percent by early adulthood (Connolly & McIsaac, 2009a).

Romantic relationships are important for adolescents and adults with disabilities also (Siebelink, de Jong, Taal, & Roelvink, 2006; Ward, Bosek, & Trimble, 2010). As one social worker explains, relationships and romantic issues are just as common among people with intellectual or developmental disabilities. Developing a secure, intimate partnership is central to psychological functioning and quality of life (Hwang, Johnston, & Smith, 2007). The World Health Organization (2017) stated in the International Classification of Functioning, Disability, and Health, a framework for measuring health and disability, that participation in romantic relationships (for example, "creating and maintaining close or romantic relationships between individuals, such as husband and wife, lovers or sexual partners"; classification d770) transcends ethnicities and cultures. However, for adolescents and adults with disabilities, understanding of and experiences with romantic relationships are different in some important ways from those of typically developing adolescents and adults. For example, one study found that even when very little time was spent with a romantic partner, adults with developmental disabilities still considered themselves to be in a romantic relationship; however, their description of what it meant to be in a romantic relationship was typical of what people without disabilities would say (Ward et al., 2010).

MICROSYSTEM

Romantic relationships are important to people with disabilities. Issues regarding sexuality and dating are regularly brought to the social work professionals we interviewed. One social worker in a small high school setting shared that all of the female students at the high school are involved romantically with someone, and most of them are dating other students with disabilities. One attraction to being involved in a romantic relationship was social status; to say "I have a boyfriend" increased one's social standing.

The challenge for social workers is in helping adolescents and adults with disabilities to be successful within those relationships—that is, successful at initiating; maintaining; and, when desired, terminating romantic relationships. One social worker working with adolescents with disabilities thinks that working with teenagers with emotional or intellectual disabilities can sometimes be like working with elementary-age kids, because they may be 16 years old but behaviorally they are five years old. In many ways, the difficulties associated with romantic relationships are not unique to those with disabilities; as youths have their first romantic and sexual experiences, they express difficulty in knowing when to get into a relationship, particularly a sexual one. They get swept away in the emotions involved with developing attachment and commitment and often have difficulty coping with a romantic breakup (Adams & Williams, 2011a). However, social workers describe the emotional responses of adolescents with disabilities in navigating romance as "amped up" compared with typical adolescent reactions, particularly for adolescents with emotional or behavioral disabilities.

Intimacy Desires

Intimacy development typically starts in adolescence and young adulthood, and this is no different for people with disabilities. The desire for intimacy within the context of a close romantic relationship is the same. A Ghanaian American young adult with cerebral palsy expressed that "I personally believe it is what we were placed on this earth to do—to love and be loved."

The difference between those with and without disabilities is in how those desires are expressed. One social worker describes one such difference as appropriate expression of desire. For example, she observes that clients with disabilities engage in exhibitionism or masturbation in front of someone else much more commonly than their peers do. A critical aspect of working with this population is making sure that the distinction between sex and intimacy is understood because they are not synonymous terms. One social worker explains that individuals with disabilities may not know that they want a relationship, but they do have a sexual interest.

One area where social workers can help adolescents and adults with disabilities is with providing concrete examples of how to achieve intimacy within the context of a romantic relationship. For example, sometimes a person with a disability might meet someone and try to hold their hand or even ask to get married. Even within established committed romantic relationships, understanding intimacy is a challenge:

> A lot of people don't know what intimacy is. Sex is much different from intimacy. So I'll have to teach them that you can't just ask . . . your wife . . . , "Hey, can we have sex?" You know, there needs to be, like, some intimacy. Massaging, petting, touching, kissing, hugging, making them feel comfortable and then having sex.

Difficulties with knowing how to achieve intimacy within a romantic relationship may occur because they may not have had good role models to understand what healthy relationships look like. One social worker believes that many people with disabilities learn about relationships from pornography or television, which is not representative of real life. The social worker explains that clients will often have sex just because that is what they think they have to do in a relationship.

Social workers describe sexual activity as a means of achieving intimacy as common among adolescents with disabilities. One social worker feels that this lends itself to less intimacy and more casual sexual encounters within their romantic relationships.

From a practical standpoint, when working with adolescents, it is sometimes difficult to identify that they are in romantic relationships. A social worker explains that her clients often do not say they have boyfriends, because they are mostly in relationships with people who they have "hooked up" with. There is general agreement that adolescents with disabilities are very sexually active, but they are more hesitant to say that this is happening within the context of a relationship. This type of relationship pattern, in which adolescents engage in a friends-with-benefits or hookup arrangement, is common of typically developing adolescents as well (Williams & Adams, 2013a, 2013b); however, typically developing adolescents are less vulnerable than adolescents with disabilities, particularly those with more severe cognitive disabilities. One social worker describes having to keep a close eye on her more cognitively impaired clients, because "they have been known to go away and hook up on campus." They want relationships but do not fully understand the parameters of them.

The casual nature of the romantic relationships of adolescents with disabilities is attributed, at least in part, to the nature of the disability itself. For example, one social worker had a student with Asperger's syndrome who had sexual interest but also felt that other people with Asperger's syndrome commonly do not want intimate relationships. Other types of disabilities limited adolescents' opportunities to experience sexual activity, even though they desired them within a context of romance. As one social worker explains,

> Physical disabilities are so impairing. I know one student in particular who is almost blind and deaf in a wheelchair. He is the most charming kid around and he wants a relationship. . . . He had a friend of the family who he fell in love with and moved to Las Vegas. They never had a relationship but in his mind he had a relationship. Because of his impairment, his thoughts are much more magical.

In general, the romantic relationships that adults with disabilities experienced are less casual than those of adolescents with disabilities. The more serious nature of intimate relationships was also true for some adolescents' relationships, which are described by social workers as "very intense." Research suggests that youths across various disability types are less likely to complete secondary education and that they are more likely to see themselves as family- rather than career-oriented (Shandra, 2011;

Shandra & Chowdhury, 2012; Wells, Sandefur, & Hogan, 2003). One of the high school social workers we interviewed was working with a dating couple. Both individuals have a disability. They had decided to come see her together after struggling with their relationship. The boy had misread the social cues of his girlfriend and was turned down while proposing marriage in the social worker's office. The social worker feels that it is not uncommon for adolescents with disabilities to want to get married (discussed in further detail in chapter 8). This sentiment concerning the highly committed nature of the relationships of some adolescents with disabilities corresponds with interviews with 15 adults with psychiatric disabilities who reported that marriage was their first step toward becoming like others (Yu & Shim, 2009). Among both youths and adults with disabilities, commitment and family orientation may hold special meaning. For example, Shandra and Chowdhury (2012) discuss how having a disability may heighten one's desire for a trusting context to experience sexual intimacy.

As for their typically developing counterparts (Adams & Williams, 2011b), gender plays a role in how intimacy is desired among people with disabilities. Research states that adolescent girls desire intimacy primarily through an emotional connection and view their relationship as more intimate than boys do (Connolly & Johnston, 1996). One social worker feels that boys desire a physical relationship more than an emotional connection. This same sentiment was brought up multiple times among social workers working with women with disabilities as well. One social worker gives an example of a woman who reported that she had never experienced intimacy within the context of a romantic relationship:

> She's been in 10-year relationships and never had intimacy. When she had sex, it was always rough sex, just achieving an orgasm. But she was also sexually abused. And so she never had that chance [to] let herself respect herself enough to gain intimacy in a relationship. She didn't feel she was deserving of that.

A young white woman with borderline personality disorder in our study shared that she often felt pressured by men to engage in sexual acts that made her uncomfortable: "Whenever I would try it, it would hurt and

I didn't like it and I'd always have pressure." Sometimes this appeared to be the result of an unconscious compromise to be able to have the experience of a romantic relationship. In other words, sexual behaviors were used as a way of wielding power within a romantic relationship, as had sometimes been done to them in the past. One social worker feels that the majority of the adolescents with disabilities that she worked with were introduced to sex at a young age and thus learned early on how to leverage sex in a relationship. Although those with disabilities are more vulnerable, this gender-based mismatch occurs within typically developing adolescents as well (Williams & Adams, 2013a).

Gender and Sexuality

Same-sex relationships were brought up by many social workers as something that adolescents and adults with disabilities experienced, particularly among girls or women. One social worker in a high school setting observes that a disproportionate number of her students with disabilities, especially girls, identify as homosexual but have a history of bisexuality. Another social worker concurred and shared that experimenting with sexual identities was a norm among her students with disabilities.

One explanation for the perceived higher rate of same-sex relationships in the adult group homes was because

> oftentimes the population is . . . segregated . . . female to female . . . male to male. So you can see a lot more homosexual behavior . . . not because the person is homosexual, simply because they don't have access to anybody else. You know, I'm sick of masturbating myself. . . . I couldn't be in a room with a woman alone to save my life but I live in this group home with three other guys and something is going to occur. So those kinds of things. So you see a lot more homosexual behavior, doesn't mean they're homosexual.

One social worker echoes this sentiment and describes many same-sex relationships occurring as a result of limited opportunities to interact with the other sex. Some of the social workers' dialogue reiterates a heteronormative discourse, suggesting heterosexuality as the norm among all of their clients. Research with youths with emotional disabilities living in a residential foster care suggests that staff tends to minimize same-sex relationships among the residents; however, the youths themselves value same-sex relationships as normative and important to them (Bermea, Rueda, & Toews, in press).

A challenge one social worker raises is in helping adolescents or adults with disabilities understand or come to terms with nonheterosexual feelings. One social worker describes a situation in which the adolescent was presenting behaviorally as gay, but he was unable to articulate his feelings and it resulted in his social isolation. She wonders if his potential reluctance to acknowledge his sexual orientation was due to the potential double discrimination he would experience on the basis of his sexuality and disability status. Regardless, some of the difficulty in social workers' ability to help resides in the fact that the person with a disability is not always aware of his or her sexual orientation.

Initiating

Initiating a romantic relationship is challenging for most adolescents and adults, but the challenges for adolescents and adults with a disability are even greater. One social worker describes witnessing

> a lot of approach-avoidance . . . not that we don't see that in the regular adolescent population, but it just seems to get amplified with these emotionally disabled students. . . . They're extremely intense and they love this other student, then they hate this other student. They're extreme in emotion.

A necessary component of a romantic relationship is that it is mutual (Connolly & McIsaac, 2011). Mutuality can be hard for those with disabilities to understand. One social worker gives an example of this:

> We had one female that was very . . . high functioning, and she's just very outgoing and a little promiscuous. And all the males focused on her and were like, "That's my girlfriend, that's my girlfriend." Even though she had no interest in them. They couldn't grasp the fact that

just because they liked her doesn't mean that she likes them. And just because they like her doesn't mean that that's their girlfriend.

Not having reciprocated romantic interest can be very frustrating. One of the social worker's clients with Asperger's syndrome told her, "I feel like I was born accidentally lonely" because he is unable to make peer connections. Another social worker speaks about her experience with an adolescent male who has physical disabilities and was frustrated about his inability to initiate a much wanted romantic relationship. Even though he was a "charmer," girls did not seem to commit to a relationship with him. This caused the boy to experience frustration and anger toward his disabilities.

Many initiation tactics adolescents and adults with disabilities use are similar to those of typically developing adolescents and adults. However, it is important to note that they may understand the meaning of these behaviors in different ways. Some may not understand that flirting has greater implications than just being a friend and that can cause problems. Initiating contact with someone of romantic interest is easier for those with certain disabilities in some ways because they "are a little bit less likely to have a boundary [than kids without disabilities]."

Relationships typically are initiated from within social contexts or through technology. Gender was not relevant in describing how adolescents or adults with disabilities initiated relationships. One social worker believes that female adolescents are just as aggressive in pursuing male adolescents, and some male adolescents are just as shy as female adolescents.

The primary way that social workers can help adolescents and adults with disabilities initiate healthy romantic relationships is through helping to improve their communication skills. As one social worker explains,

> They have low communication skills. Healthy communication about how to get to know one another [is needed]. Regardless of disability, they have lost the ability to communicate. A lot of it is online and texting. So, after the first couple times . . . it goes to the physical. . . . And these notes look like elementary [school]. "Do you want to hook up with me? Yes or no."

Maintaining

The difficulty with communication trickled into the ability to maintain relationships once they were initiated. As one social worker explains, "They will seriously be in a relationship and not talk to one another." Part of this difficulty is developmental, particularly for adolescents in romantic relationships (Adams & Williams, 2011a, 2011b), but part is due to the nature of the disability itself. One social worker explains that this results in much shorter relationships than is typical for youths:

> Their dating experience is very skewed by their inability to maintain relationships. That's part of their diagnosis. I get students in here all the time talking about, you know, their thoughts and feeling regarding their relationship. They are not different from students without disabilities. They have the same needs and wants but the ability is different. Their relationship is, like, two days, while a normal adolescent would be, like, two weeks.

Another social worker attributes the longevity of the relationship to the severity of the disability. That is, the more impairing the disability the shorter the romantic relationships are:

> The higher functioning [adolescents have] very typical teenage behavior. They do everything from flirting to dating, though I don't see a lot of long-term relationships. The severely [impaired], they have new girlfriends or boyfriends every week, because they are more like a five- or six-year-old.

Below is an example of how a mental health disability affected the otherwise healthy romantic relationship of one social worker's client:

> Someone I saw yesterday deals with PTSD and depression and she cannot trust her boyfriend. She has a lot of jealousy issues. Meanwhile, balancing this relationship, she's trying to balance her own mind. She has a lot of internal conflict. Again, her internal dialogue is very negative. She has panic attacks and so here she is trying to find some balance within her own life. So it's very hard for her to have a healthy relationship with her partner. When he actually treats her

well and has treated her better than any other person. But she's unable to see these things because she feels so unstable.

Two primary reasons for shorter relationships were enhanced emotional responses and the speed with which they entered the relationship to begin with. One social worker describes this as romantic relationships "at hyperspeed." The enhanced emotional responses, such as crying, screaming, and yelling, continue into adulthood and seem to cause instability in relationships. A young white woman with an emotional disability describes her relationship with an on-again/off-again boyfriend as tumultuous:

> It was a real breakup. I moved all my [stuff] out. We had a couple altercations of screaming fighting. We ended up . . . finally breaking up at the end of April, literally the day before Stagecoach, and then the [guy]came with me to Stagecoach trying to win me back. He did end up wooing me within a month. We're back together.

The relationship itself, as alluded to previously, is thus both casual and intense. A social worker working with those with primarily emotional disabilities shares that extreme mood swings complicate relationships. Adolescent girls with emotional disabilities, in particular, often experience mood swings in which they love someone one moment and never want to see them again the next moment.

Another social worker highlighted adolescent girls' heightened intensity in their romantic relationships as a result of poorer communication skills and reduced peer support. The high emotional intensity is not limited to adolescents with disabilities. Social workers in group homes with adults also describe "a lot of drama" around relationships:

> [They'll] be exchanging little trinkets . . . Valentine's Day, they have sanctioned dances and going there. So it's a lot like perpetual *Beverly Hills 90210*. There's a lot of drama. This person broke up with this person and now they're dating that person.

Another social worker describes the relationship issues that come up as something expected of adolescent dating relationships, even though the clients she works with are adults.

A big challenge for many adults with disabilities is figuring out how to spend time with their romantic partner appropriately. One social worker illustrated this in the following story:

> Most of them don't quite grasp . . . there's a time and place for everything. . . . The workplace is not the time to cultivate a romantic relationship. And typically, though, that's the area that they see each other most. Because then they'll return to their homes where they live and they don't see each other, so they'll continue the conversation by the phones, sometimes have issues with the telephones, issues in the [group] home, hog a phone but they have to understand that if they have a vocation . . . that that's their primary responsibility. . . . [In places where] they have dances . . . that gives . . . an opportunity for them to have a venue to go to. There are places like Special Olympics where they can bowl together or play basketball together or whatever. . . . And they could call each other, maybe meet for a hamburger somewhere.

As mentioned previously, coaching is usually needed to help adults with disabilities develop intimacy within the relationship.

Romantic relationships tend to be conceptualized by social workers who work with adolescents with disabilities as casual because they are not often exclusive. It is notable that sexual intercourse is separated conceptually from the romantic relationship itself. This is consistent with previous research in which adolescents consider nonsexual behaviors as "cheating" (Williams & Hickle, 2011).

Terminating Relationships

Relationship breakups occur frequently across the adolescent years (Connolly & McIsaac, 2009a). Most breakups are initiated by girls. Adolescents will typically decide to end a relationship when they no longer enjoy, share intimate feelings with, or experience sexual attraction for their partner. Romantic breakups have been linked to negative psychosocial outcomes (for example, distress, depression, symptoms of grief).

Adolescents and adults with disabilities experience frequent break-ups, given both greater participation and reduced time spent in dating relationships. They are also at risk for experiencing greater distress following a breakup. One social worker explains that a breakup of a relationship is the most common reason that her clients feel suicidal. She emphasizes that this is heightened for adolescents with emotional disabilities. However, one social worker noticed that this is not true for everyone; some can get over relationships easily.

The majority of social workers describe relationship problems and breakups as one of the biggest threats to the emotional well-being of adolescents with disabilities. Two social workers referred to adolescence as a time when individuals experience life in a dichotomous nature. One believes that those with intellectual and emotional disabilities experience only concrete thinking, which exacerbates dichotomous thinking:

> Because of the issues of the black-and-white thinking of that "this was my true love." "How long have you been going out?" "Eh, two weeks." I mean, I have an ED [emotionally disabled] girl who . . . I've worked with since her freshmen year and this is her junior year, and it's so neat to see her development now. "Eh, I just broke up with this guy. I didn't need him anymore." . . . A year ago, she would've been out cutting on herself.

MESOSYSTEM

Romantic relationships are embedded within systems outside the relationship. Many of these settings have explicit rules around dating (for example, at school, in the group home), but other systems (for example, family, caregivers) have less clear or conflicting perspectives.

Structural

Challenges

One challenge for adolescents and adults with disabilities related to romantic relationships is that they have to exist within the rules of the settings in which they reside or spend time in. For adolescents, structural barriers occur in the school setting. Some schools have specific rules about dating and what is allowed on campus. One barrier one social worker describes is simply access to school, which may be thwarted when a romantic relationship fails. She describes this as follows:

> A lot of the girls, if they had [a] boyfriend who dropped out, [it] would put a lot of pressure on them not to go to school. If the boyfriend dropped out, then they would sabotage. It's competition. He's afraid that she's going to meet someone else. Like, if they were responsible for taking them to school.

Even in adult settings, many structural challenges exist. One social worker in a group home explains that even for her adult clients,

> they can't have a, like, a normal date because they have safeguards in place, there's always someone like a staff member with those individuals. When we're guardian over somebody, we're obviously involved because they can't make all of their decisions. You or I can go out and have fun by ourselves. These individuals have oversight staff with them.

Furthermore, in group home settings, extra rules are in place for those who have had a sexually inappropriate past. One social worker explains that the protocol for those individuals includes constant supervision, especially if they have a girlfriend or boyfriend come over. If there was no previous history of impropriety, adults could have the option of being alone. However, because they often have medical needs, they rarely have opportunities to be alone, as staff need to accompany them.

Other group homes have more rigid rules beyond supervision that prevent adults from developing romantic relationships. If social workers witness romantic activity in these settings, they are required to complete an incident report. One social worker explains that this makes sense for adults who are not able to cognitively consent to a romantic relationship, but it compromises the privacy and respect for those who can. She explains,

> I kind of get crazy when we get those incident reports where, "Oh they were holding hands and [I] tried to separate them" . . . well . . .

why? If you have . . . somebody with dementia diagnosis who can't give consent, that's a whole different story. But if you have people with the capacity, they're still adults and they still have their needs. And you need to give them the privacy, you know . . . for whatever they want to do.

Resiliencies

The majority of social workers in adult group homes feel that the structure is set up to support romantic relationships. For example, one social worker observes that although individuals need to ask permission to access their financial resources, they are able to do so within a romantic context.

To support adults with disabilities and their intimacy rights, it is important that the structure of their residence is set up to support those rights. One social worker illustrates that when the structure is not supportive, you not only risk distress to the individual, but you potentially create more problems within your setting:

Programming or the daily routine . . . lack . . . the support that inhibits these relationships. When you cut that part out of somebody else's life, they're going to try and meet that need in some way and then oftentimes that's when you find that inappropriate sexual behavior.

The social worker also describes that on a rare occasion, those who are served in supportive living are given an opportunity to rent a hotel room for a night to have alone time with their intimate partner. However, support staff is available in the hotel lobby as needed.

Parents and Family

Parents and family members are usually explicitly involved in their child's romantic relationships; at a minimum they are informed of the relationship, and at the maximum they are actively part of the romantic relationship itself. In general, social workers feel that family members are generally not supportive of romantic relationships, even among adults. As one social worker working with adults with disabilities states,

> You get two different things. You get people [who] are overly involved to where, like, "I'm dating Stacy but I'm also dating Stacy's mom because Stacy's mom is her guardian. Stacy's mom gets to say everything that occurs with Stacy." Then you get the people to where they don't want to introduce sex or relationships to their adult child because if they do that then all of a sudden he's going to be some insatiable sexual deviant. It's controlled to an unrealistic extent.

Social workers in school settings also feel that parents play a big role in their child's romantic relationships. Although this has the potential to be positive, social workers often feel parental support is lacking or that the family system is already in distress and incapable of serving that supportive role:

> A lot of my kids have family problems so the support system isn't there so they aren't able to go home and talk to their parents openly about, you know, if they have any sexually related issues. Those kids don't have enough guidance or support, and they're going to their friends, which, you know, isn't the best source of information.

This is sometimes stressful to the social workers at school because they feel that they are not able to give all of the support that their students need.

When there is open communication between parents and social workers, however, there is an opportunity to see that support across these systems can go a long way to help those with disabilities. As one social worker in a school setting explains,

> This is a mildly intellectually disabled girl . . . says, "My mom told me that if I was going to have sex, I needed to come to her and tell her and that she would get me on birth control." And I said, "Well . . . would you actually do that?" And she goes, "Oh yeah, yeah . . . my mom would be really upset and it would break trust if I, you know, started having sex and I didn't tell her."

Educators

Finally, some of the barriers lie in the beliefs of the educators or social workers themselves. This is critical because although adolescents and adults with disabilities may have the desire and the ability to initiate a sexual or romantic relationship, they need support to help navigate the complexities of romantic relationships in a way that they can understand. One social worker observes that educators may not believe that adolescents and adults with disabilities have the cognitive ability to understand sexual health education:

> Sometimes educators think that they don't have the cognition to really understand about sex or to want it or to pursue it, but they have hormones just like everyone else, and they have desire and they start to understand that. So they are sexually active without really realizing or having a complete understanding of what that really means.

Social Workers

Social workers are often put in the position of having to serve as mediators between systems that are conflicting or even between conflicts within the same system. The conflict may occur between structural requirements and the broader acceptance of people with disabilities having a relationship. Social workers can help serve in this area by educating others that it is okay for two people to hold hands or kiss on the cheek if they can consent.

Social workers can also work to educate family systems about romantic relationships. One social worker describes a situation in which she attempted to facilitate communication between her adult client with disabilities and her legal guardian about her client's desires to get married. The social worker was prepared to make arrangements for a commitment ceremony, but the guardian was adamantly against it. So although social workers try to work within these systems to get their clients what they want, they are not always successful.

In other cases, social workers are successful at navigating around systems that prevent people with disabilities from being together. One social worker describes a situation in which two people wanted to be romantically involved, but they lived in a group home that prohibited cohabitation:

> We would move one of the people out but they could date. They could date each other and toward the end, probably the last five or six years,

> if they wanted to go to a hotel, we would do that. . . . Some people, if they're severely intellectually disabled or moderately intellectually disabled, would need protection from the community or maybe they're not as appropriate as they should be so . . . we would send a staff person in there in the adjoining room just to kind of shadow them.

Sometimes social workers feel that it is a daily struggle and that they have to manipulate the system to help their clients.

EXOSYSTEM AND MACROSYSTEM

The message from the larger system that youths and adults with disabilities receive is that romantic relationships are not for them. There needs to be a greater cultural acceptance of people with disabilities having relationships. Although relationships may be initiated, maintained, and terminated differently among people with disabilities than they are in the general population, the way that people with disabilities experience love and romantic relationships is essentially the same. A certain perception of disability excludes those who are disabled from participating—the perception that "'oh yeah, that person's disabled, they shouldn't have a boyfriend,' or 'they don't need a boyfriend or a girlfriend.' That kind of thing . . . it's the culture of 'able' bodies seeing the disability as a deterrent." This quote reflects the societal structures described in the social model of disability and crip theory (McRuer, 2006; Oliver, 1996).

The cultural message around adolescent romantic relationships is that they are short and physically intense and lack emotional intimacy. Adolescents and adults with disabilities are not immune to the cultural messages around gender and what that means in a romantic relationship. For example, there is a cultural pressure for boys to see girls as a conquest. Youths' easy access to the Internet and pornography sets unhealthy relationship expectations.

Social workers can work toward combating this negative messaging that exists in our culture. As one social worker stated, "They need to change the message that they are getting and . . . whatever it is it should be put on their cognitive level."

IMPLICATIONS FOR SOCIAL WORK PRACTICE

Romantic relationships are important to adolescents and adults with disabilities. One way that social workers can help to support the development of romantic relationships is to first help the clients that they work with understand that it is their right to participate in romantic relationships if they desire to do so. Sometimes, however, this also opens the door for those with disabilities to make poor choices.

Social workers can help by making sure adolescents and adults with disabilities are supported across their ecosystem. This can be achieved by examining the policies within their work or school settings, opening the lines of communication with caregivers, and helping individuals to secure the support that they need to be successful at navigating the complexities of romantic relationships. In addition, it is critical that the treatment plan is developed with support staff contribution. Finally, social workers can help within the romantic relationship itself by giving the individual concrete and specific ideas, such as suggestions for replacements of inappropriate behaviors.

CONCLUSION

Intimacy is a basic human need. Adolescents and adults with disabilities have the same desires as those without disabilities: to experience love, to achieve intimacy, and to participate in romantic relationships. Developing a secure intimate partnership is central to psychological functioning and quality of life and is a right of all individuals. As one social worker observes, "Whether you have a disability or not, you're still hardwired with sexual needs. Those sexual needs are going to vary per individual, but (a) recognize they are there [and] (b) support the person in meeting their needs in a healthy and safe way."

5

Sex Education

Approximately half of U.S. teenagers have had sex by the time they are in high school (Eaton et al., 2011). Adolescents with a range of disabilities, including cognitive, physical, and emotional, engage in dating and sexual activity at similar or higher rate as other adolescents (Donenberg et al., 2012; Mandell et al., 2008; Murphy et al., 2006). In addition, as discussed more in chapter 7, adolescents with disabilities are more likely to experience pregnancy and to parent than other teenagers (Shandra, 2011). Both of these findings indicate a need for sex education among adolescents with disabilities. Although the majority of schools offer one form or another of sexual education, the content and timing vary considerably (Kann, Brener, McManus, & Wechsler, 2012), and adolescents with disabilities often do not receive appropriate sexual health education as a result of abstinence-only policies, exclusion via special education, or the provision of information that is not tailored to their learning needs (Shakespeare, 2000; Stanger-Hall & Hall, 2011; Swango-Wilson, 2011). This reflects a larger dialogue within society that assumes that youths with disabilities are asexual or considers their sexual behavior as less acceptable, unsafe, or inappropriate (Murphy et al., 2006; Shandra & Chowdhury, 2012). This way of thinking ostracizes people with disabilities from full participation in society and sexual citizenship, robbing them of important aspects of their personhood (Winges-Yanez, 2014). Although we typically think of sexual health education as occurring in schools, education also comes from other informal sources. Youths with disabilities are also less likely than adolescents without disabilities to learn about sexual activity, reproductive processes, and potential sexual outcomes (for example, pregnancy or sexually transmitted infections [STIs]) from their peers, parents, or doctors (Blum, Resnick, Nelson, & St. Germaine, 1991).

A child develops sexual identity as part of global identity during adolescence, a process that continues to be shaped into the young adult, adult, and older adult years (Collins, 2003). However, as we carefully analyzed data from social workers serving each of these age cohorts, some similar themes emerged with respect to sexual health education. First, people with disabilities receive insufficient sexual health information, often as a result of societal (for example, policies), parental, or practitioner discomfort. Second, responsibility to educate people with disabilities is often deferred to others (for example, parent to school, social worker to school nurse). Third, social workers' roles in serving people with disabilities toward sexual health is often in response to problematic sexual behaviors. Finally, social workers highlight the need for disability-specific resources to encompass sexual and relationship health education, as well as prevention of STIs, pregnancy, and sexual assault. Differences emerge in social workers' experiences serving various age populations, which will be discussed later in the chapter.

We outline this chapter in accordance with ecological systems theory, which considers the macrosystem (for example, encompassing beliefs surrounding disability, policies) as a metaconstruct. In other words, we approach the discussion of microsystemic influences exerted by and on the child from the stance that these attitudes and actions are understood only within larger societal policies and discourses concerning sexuality and disability.

MICROSYSTEM

Social workers recommend a positive and proactive approach to reaching people with disabilities with appropriately tailored information about sexual health; to the contrary, social workers serving all age cohorts feel that people with disabilities are not receiving sufficient sexual health information. This lack of information starts in the home environment. Social workers feel that this reflects a discomfort with the topic among parents. Other research has found that discussion of sexuality with children is difficult for parents of typically developing youths (Christensen et al., 2016); social workers explain how parental discussions at home are even more difficult amid a range of challenges related to disability. As a social worker describes, not having someone to openly and safely discuss sexual feelings, bodily changes, and sexual desires presents a challenge for children with disabilities:

> Again when I think back to some of the individuals that I've worked with [that had] intellectual disability or autism or even physical disabilities or impairments, and that's been a really challenging time in their lives for those individuals because they don't have the same ability to kind of understand or to have someone explain to them what is occurring in their body and what those changes are and that they're normal and kind of a bright and normal part of development, and so it can be a really scary time for them.

Other research that has looked at parents' perspectives has found that they want more sexual health education from practitioners serving their child with a disability (Ballan, 2012). An important part of working with youths and families is that social workers in our study advocate for people with disabilities as equal sexual citizens, recognizing and honoring their human need for connection and intimacy. Social workers often recognize these values as lying at the heart of our profession. However, children receive subtle or overt messages from parents that they are not capable of having intimate relationships.

Although social workers serving children with disabilities voice the importance of having someone to explain basic sexual health, it was important that they also educate parents concerning the child's ability and deservedness to forge intimate partnerships later in life. What is more, the contexts discussed in chapter 3, including the development of self-esteem, social skills, and a positive sexual and relationship self, contribute to a child's ability to make good sexual and relationship decisions in adolescence, adulthood, and older adulthood. You may note that much of the dialogue from social workers concerning the microsystem comes from those serving children. Social workers serving adolescents with disabilities focus much of their discussion about sexual health education on pregnancy (see chapter 7) and on meso- and macro-level work (described later in this chapter).

Social workers describe many challenges to working with individuals with disabilities and their caregivers, and when asked about any unique training, tools, or materials used in provision of sexuality education, they feel that most of what they had learned resulted from on-the-job training. Many state that they could benefit from additional training or support in working with people with disabilities. Those serving children reflect on their use of foundational training, continuing education, and fundamental social work skills and values, such as self-determination. They also rely on books and games often highlighting the need for disability-specific resources to encompass sexual and relationship health. Social workers note they have creatively adapted tools to meet the unique sexual and relational health needs of children with disabilities. However, they reflected on the necessity for more specialized tools:

> It's taking material, curriculum, tools or skills and, um, fine-tuning them to apply to children with disabilities. There isn't, to me, . . . a sufficient menu of options for children with disabilities, especially very young children. And so, you have to end up building in your own accommodations.

The data from our study are promising in that the social workers interviewed are enacting various roles to strengthen healthy sexuality among people with disabilities across the lifespan. They use a wide variety of practice modalities, often referring to creative and resourceful practice tools, as well as their reliance on foundational social work skills stemming from a deep commitment to social work values (NASW, 2015a). However, some dialogue also reiterates concerns regarding the neglect of sexual health advancement. As Ballan (2012) states at the conclusion of her qualitative study with parents of children with autism spectrum disorder, "Too often, the discussion when it does occur with providers, is restricted to problematic sexual behaviors exhibited by a child. Such discussions are reactive versus proactive and fail to contextualize the normative developmental sexual needs of children with the disorder" (p. 683). Social workers who work with children voice that sexual education often occurs as a result of referral for societally unacceptable, inappropriate, or unsafe sexual behaviors; thus, rather than viewing their work as promoting positive sexuality, their work reflects intervention.

Social workers serving children with disabilities should be familiar with how disability may affect developing sexuality. For example, youths with autism spectrum disorder have been found to know less about sexuality and to display more sexually expressive (that is, often deemed inappropriate) behaviors than their peers (Ray et al., 2004; Stokes & Kaur, 2005). In addition, sensory needs may lead to sensory-motivated sexual behavior deemed inappropriate (Nichols & Blakeley-Smith, 2010). Social deficits that correspond with the disability may cause a child to not differentiate between public and private spaces, to misread other's intentions, to act impulsively without accurate assessment of the context and social environment, or to involve themselves in risky or even illegal sexual situations as a result of desiring relationships and acceptance (see Ballan, 2012). These factors shaping a child's developing sexuality are largely reflective of society and point to the need for disability awareness education for children, adults, and professionals. As Shakespeare (2000) writes, "The barriers to the sexual expression of disabled people are primarily to do with the society in which we live, not the bodies with which we are endowed" (p. 161).

The finding that those serving children and youths with disabilities are asked to promote sexual health only in the context of sexually problematic behaviors (for example, public masturbation, pregnancy) is concerning from a social model of disability perspective. When working to educate children concerning sexual health and the appropriateness of social context, social workers should counter messages of shame and instead work to normalize sexuality and promote positive feelings. Social workers serving adolescents can shift their focus to include family planning in addition to pregnancy prevention, particularly given their reports of multiple pregnancies and desires among this population to have children. In fact, we know from a national longitudinal study of youths that adolescents with a range of disabilities are more likely to conceive and become parents by the age of 20 than those without disabilities (Shandra, 2011). Attention should be directed to both male and female youths' responsibility to family planning and potential for pregnancy. Social workers should seek consultation regarding complex and often ethical issues at the intersection of an individual's and the couple's self-determination. These complex issues include desires to parent and a number of socioemotional, physical, and cognitive impairments that can affect their decisions to use contraceptives or to parent a child. Shandra and Chowdhury (2012) found that youths with emotional and learning conditions were actually more likely to discuss birth control the first time they had sex compared with youths without learning and emotional disabilities. However, the content and quality of these conversations is unknown. We do know that adolescents with disabilities often drop out of school earlier than other youths (Shandra, 2011; Shandra & Chowdhury, 2012); this points to the need to reach them with appropriately and individually tailored sexual health information early.

MESOSYSTEM

Many social workers in our study describe their role as empowering families to discuss sexuality and relationship health more proactively with youths. However, social workers sometimes seem to delegate the responsibility of sex education to the parents. Few programs exist to help facilitate this conversation. We are aware of only one such program, "Growing Up Aware" (Ballan, 2012), which teaches parents how to be sexuality educators for children with autism spectrum disorder.

Parents may not reach out to community resources except in situations perceived as sexually problematic. Rather, social workers should encourage parents to foster their children's sexual and relationship health from a young age and throughout their youth. However, they should recognize the societal stigma attached and not only encourage parents to advocate but also directly advocate on their behalf for an improved system that embraces individuals with disabilities as full sexual citizens.

Social workers also believe that other school professionals should be responsible for sex education for adolescents with disabilities. However, they express that school professionals can often be guarded when it comes to providing this kind of support. Many school district policies restrict sex education to abstinence only, which covers pubertal changes without discussion of prevention or contraction of sexually transmitted diseases. This makes it difficult for social workers and other school professionals alike to provide adolescents with disabilities with appropriate sex education. Constraints stemming from abstinence-only education, discussed later as part of macro-level influences, hamper school social workers' and other helping professionals' ability to effectively educate adolescents with disabilities. Social workers are often forced to sidestep such policies and help the best they can. For example, social workers frame their discussions with adolescents carefully, to circumvent sexual education restrictions or via indirect questioning:

> Sometimes I feel hesitant about what I can share. Um, and it's hard because the school obviously promotes abstinence, so it's kind of . . . it's hard in regard to, you know, I'll ask somebody, "I hope you're using something," and they say, "Yes."

Others opened themselves up more fully for such discussions despite the policies in place. One social worker admits that she would not tell the administration that she is talking about sex in the group that she runs. Some talk about sex only behind closed doors in their offices, where discussions with clients are protected with confidentiality. Others couch their tendency to do so as a moral and ethical responsibility within the social work profession itself. The following quote illustrates a felt hesitation to admit fault in going against district and school policies:

> I think the social workers, just from our own ethical perspectives, we believe strongly that if, you know, we have a student that's struggling

with something that we need to provide the services for them . . . even though we still have to go over—we still are employees of a district that believes in abstinence only. So . . . we're just kind of walking that tightrope of, you know, our own social work values and then the policies that the district has in place. So it's kind of a hard little rope to walk but we do the best that we can.

MACROSYSTEM

There is disagreement concerning who should educate youths about sexual health, reflecting a larger societal discomfort with the topic in the United States. Scholarship and policies have reflected this trend. There's a distinct lack of research addressing sexuality as a normative developmental milestone, and particularly assessing the benefits associated with healthy sexuality for youths (Harden, 2014). Most studies point to risk factors for youths with disabilities, such as pregnancy or sexually transmitted diseases (Christensen et al., 2016). Dialogue from the interviews we conducted evidence a central focus on the importance of imparting relationship skills necessary for youths to have healthy intimate sexual and romantic relationships, including disability-related challenges that affect their ability to do so (for example, self-esteem challenges and body image; see chapter 3). However, a shift is apparent in adolescent, adult, and older adult interviews. Within these groups, there is a strong perception that the purpose of sexual health education for individuals with disabilities is to prevent STIs, pregnancies, and sexual assault. It is interesting that this reflects debates in the United States over abstinence-only versus comprehensive forms of sexual health education. Although there is little variation in social workers' voiced need for comprehensive sexual health education for these age groups, their direct practice serving individuals of reproductive age reflects lived contexts in which they often come to serve them (for example, situations of pregnancy). Here, we discuss each of these funding streams, as well as new directions that also seek to incorporate and centralize relationship skills, of utmost importance if sexual health education is to be successful.

In the United States, there are debates over two primary types of funding for sexual health education. The first, commonly referred to as "comprehensive sex education," includes discussion of contraception and protection where it is otherwise omitted (Constantine, Jerman, & Huang, 2007). It has been argued that to be truly comprehensive, sexual health education should also (a) help individuals make safe and healthy sexual decisions within relationship contexts; (b) encourage positive family–caregiver communication about sexuality; (c) teach individuals about intimate partner (and other forms of relational) violence to include sexual abuse; (d) provide medically accurate information that helps individuals to understand the benefits of abstinence, as well as the benefits and risks of various forms of contraceptives; and (e) help individuals to understand the risks of sexual activity when using drugs and alcohol (SIECUS, 2009). Although content and tone vary across curricula, we assert that these emphases should consider sexuality as a positive aspect of development and frame it as such (see Harden, 2014, for a "sex-positive" framework). Increased funding is moving toward comprehensive sexual education, with $41.1 million awarded to states and territories in fiscal year 2014 (Family and Youth Services Bureau, 2015b). Parents largely prefer that youths receive this type of education (Constantine et al., 2007), as do social workers in our study. In fact, social workers exhibit a strong desire for youths to be educated comprehensively about their sexuality, arguing for a removal of abstinence-only restrictions in the classroom and direct practice settings. Regardless of desires for youths to remain sexually abstinent, they feel that reality does not mirror such policies: "When you say abstinence only, they will laugh in your face. They know it's a joke."

However, many youths and adults have been educated according to abstinence-only funding streams, in which educators must teach that sex before marriage is likely to have negative psychological and health consequences and that abstinence is the only way to completely avoid undesirable sex-related outcomes (Family and Youth Services Bureau, 2015a). The Abstinence Education Grant Program allotted $35.8 million to 39 states and territories in fiscal year 2014 (Family and Youth Services Bureau, 2015a). Although these funding streams are separate and often thought about in an either/or manner, it is helpful to note that they are not mutually exclusive. For example, abstinence is taught within comprehensive curricula, sometimes even to a considerable degree (Jeffries, Dodge,

Bandiera, & Reece, 2010). However, in addition to the critical inclusion of components such as gender identity, sexual orientation, and contraception, comprehensive sexual education allows for greater depth of coverage of relationship-building skills (SIECUS, 2009), which social workers think, and we agree, are absolutely necessary to any sexual education agenda.

Youths with disabilities are affected by high school sex education policies, although schools may forgo sex education with this population. Swango-Wilson (2011) found that young adults with intellectual or developmental disabilities reflecting on their experience with sexual education in school reported that they either did not receive or did not understand it. This sentiment is reiterated by a social worker who describes how children with disabilities received the same sexual health videos and discussion that the other kids received:

> I am not aware of, like, you asked me about the curriculum for special ed kids' parents, and what kind of sexual classes they would provide to the parents. I know that what we do is the fourth and fifth grade movie presentation on your child's human development and the changes that we go through. To what capacity the kids understand, and what is offered to the parents, I'm not aware of.

Another study of adolescents in special education in Sweden found that the majority of participants found it difficult to remember if they had received sexual education or not. Of those who could remember receiving it, many reported that it was difficult to comprehend (Löfgren-Mårtenson, 2011). Despite unique challenges, sex education for adolescents with disabilities often mirrors normative development and assumes that intellectual, physical, and psychological growth are proceeding at the same rate (Tissot, 2009). Adolescents with disabilities are, however, entitled to adapted sexual education and services according to IDEA (2004). Of note, this policy conceptualizes disability broadly to encompass multiple disability types (for example, emotional, physical, mental, and intellectual disorders) within a unifying service delivery framework. IDEA does not specify that education about sexuality should be adapted for students with disabilities; however, it does mandate that education be adapted to meet students' needs. We find that social workers, mirroring IDEA, serve individuals with a wide range of disability types and levels of severity. Sexual and relationship health education policies are needed to attend to diverse learning needs (for example, individual sexual health education plans; Barnard-Brak et al., 2014). However, youths often slip through the cracks. Social workers feel that a lack of funding results in an overabundance of clients on their caseloads or a lack entirely of social work services for certain districts. Social work services are quickly cut in times of economic hardship, resulting in a reduction in support service staff and often including only part-time appointments:

> We have myself, who deals with the high-profile difficult kids, and we have another social worker part-time here to provide additional support to special ed students. So last night in the board meeting, they are eliminating two of the three positions.

Time restrictions are even more pressing given the additional services needed by adolescents with special needs. Sexual and dating issues often fall to the bottom of a long list of other priorities. Social workers discuss these missed opportunities as often significant events in the lives of the adolescents with whom they work: "I guess I don't talk to them enough. . . . There's no time for that. And then you hear that they're pregnant. Oh, we missed that window."

Schools may underutilize funding streams for relationship skill building that are available aside from those allotted for sexual health education specifically. President Obama signed into effect the Every Student Succeeds Act, which replaces the No Child Left Behind Act. Of importance to sexual and relationship education is that this act provides funding for activities supporting safe and healthy students (Every Student Succeeds Act, 2015, Title IV, Sec. 4108, C-iv). Schools may use these funds to teach relationship and communication skills, including those on how to be safe. School districts receiving more than $30,000 must use at least 20 percent of their funding on a minimum of one activity or program that helps students be safe and healthy (Every Student Succeeds Act, 2015). Curricula such as Love Notes by the Dibble Institute were designed for youths at risk for teenage pregnancy or for youths who are already parenting and include modules designed to teach youths how to have healthy relationships, to build communication skills, and to understand how to be safe (for example, teenage dating violence prevention). This program may be efficacious with adolescents with disabilities given earlier discussion concerning a need for family planning. Although the program was recently added to the National Registry for Evidence-Based Programs (U.S. Department of Health and Human Services, 2016), it is in need of adaptation and evaluation for youths with disabilities. Another program available to practitioners is the Dibble Institute's Mike's Crush, which teaches relationship and communication skills to youths with autism and intellectual disabilities (Dibble Institute, n.d.). Another, Friendships and Dating, was designed for teenagers (16 and older) and adults (UAA Center for Human Development, 2017) but studied with adults with intellectual and developmental disabilities (Ward, Atkinson, Smith, & Windsor, 2013; Ward, Windsor, & Atkinson, 2012). Results indicated a decrease in interpersonal partner violence and increase in the number of friends to have fun with (Ward et al., 2013; Ward et al., 2012). Finally, the Family Life and Sexual Health sexual education curriculum was designed for youths with disabilities, but the reader is advised to read Winges-Yanez's (2014) call for advocacy on behalf of social workers in changing the dialogue promoted by this and other sexual health curricula toward full sexual empowerment of people with disabilities.

As mentioned, an important discussion point when we think about sexual health education is that adolescents with a range of both severe and mild disabilities are less likely to finish high school (Shandra, 2011; Shandra & Chowdhury, 2012). In addition to IDEA (2004), policies are needed that address sexual health specifically and that expand beyond high school education. Aside from classroom-based sexual education, community resources may also provide free or reduced-cost sexual health and family planning services for youths, although providers may feel somewhat uncomfortable administering information to youths with disabilities (Rohleder, 2010). This stigma may limit the availability of resources, and continued controversy over federal funding of Planned Parenthood may result in its defunding, in turn also limiting access to affordable birth control, medical exams, and sex education (Cunningham, 2017; Planned Parenthood, 2017). Furthermore, health educators receive very little training on pregnancy, HIV, other STIs, and violence prevention (Centers for Disease Control and Prevention, 2000). Trained social workers can play critically important roles in delivering sexual health services to individuals with disabilities and their caregivers.

IMPLICATIONS FOR SOCIAL WORK PRACTICE

Individuals with disabilities are often stigmatized in various ways across the ecosystem, the result of which is oppression and alienation from full sexual citizenship. Social workers can serve as advocates at each level for their full inclusion, recognizing the barriers that youths and families face in obtaining medically accurate, understandable, and positive messages about sexual health.

Social workers serving individuals of all ages agree that more services and education are necessary both for themselves and for youths and families concerning sexual health education. However, many social workers also demonstrate attitudes of discomfort in administering this education and opt instead to refer their clients to other professionals. Some of their reasons for doing so result from policy barriers, particularly for social workers serving adolescents in school settings. Barriers to meeting the sexual health needs of adults and older adults with disabilities are similar to those described by social workers serving children and adolescents; specifically, such social workers find that sexual health education content often needs modification, that consequences of sexual intercourse are often not understood within the contexts of what it means to be in an intimate or healthy relationship, and that it is difficult to promote positive sexuality when individuals often come to work with social workers in contexts labeled as sexually problematic.

Although these similar themes are reiterated by social workers serving various age groups, different practice modalities are suggested. Social workers serving children discuss the importance of educating parents about children as sexual beings and creating peer environments among typically abled youths that respect disability as an aspect of diversity. Some recommend starting conversations early with children and parents concerning sexual health, including body parts, reproduction, sexual feelings, and how the child is fully capable and expected to go on to experience meaningful intimate partnerships in life. Practitioners discuss using creative means of working in direct-practice settings with youths, using Internet-based tools and sexual health books that they adapt uniquely for the child or adult with whom they are working. Social workers who serve older adults report the need to run support groups that normalize sexual activity during the later years and that address different forms of sexual intimacy (for example, hand holding, fondling).

CONCLUSION

Sex education begins for most youths in school, and IDEA (2004) mandates that education accommodations be made for people with disabilities. Whether in schools or in out-of-school settings, sex education needs to be adapted and provided for youths with disabilities, while taking individual developmental timing, contexts, disability type, and severity into consideration. Sex education can and should continue to be provided for adults and older adults in a similar manner. Social workers can (a) continue to provide individualized sex education for their clients with disabilities and encourage early conversations in the home; (b) advocate for their school districts to seek funding for and provide adapted, comprehensive sex education for students with disabilities; and (c) work with families and other professionals to support the sex education of their clients with disabilities throughout the life course.

6

Romantic Relationship Vulnerability and Victimization

A high school social worker expresses concerns that people with disabilities are more vulnerable to victimization:

> They are sexually active without really realizing or having a complete understanding of what that really means. You know, especially if they're easily led by social behavior, how simple would it be to say, "Everyone does this, it's what you do when you're friends." . . . "Oh, let me touch you here."

She, like many other social workers, felt that poor self-esteem and decision-making skills were among the key risk factors contributing to the heightened sexual vulnerability of people with disabilities in both committed and uncommitted romantic and sexual contexts. Many social workers describe numerous circumstances in which adolescents came to them with issues concerning sexuality and romantic relationships, several of which included current sexual victimization. This supports the research finding that people with disabilities are more likely than others to experience being physically forced to have sex (Alriksson-Schmidt, Armour, & Thibadeau, 2010). Social workers voice the belief that, in conjunction with the disability itself, prior victimization made it difficult to untangle complex risk factors that heightened their clients' risk for further abuse. Such vulnerabilities that social workers describe, and that clients experienced in our work and research, represent overlapping and mutually influential microsystem, mesosystem, exosystem, and macrosystems as described by Bronfenbrenner's (1979) ecological systems theory.

MICROSYSTEM
Individual Level: Self-Esteem and Decision Making

Generally, social workers feel that people with disabilities, especially female adolescents, do not have the self-esteem or the decision-making skills to say no in sexual situations. Poor self-esteem, limited cognitive abilities, and impaired decision making have been associated with sexual vulnerability in previous research. Doyle (2008) found that adolescents with learning disabilities were more vulnerable to forced sex because of their high prevalence of low self-esteem. In addition, whereas people with physical disabilities experience more sexual assault than people without disabilities, people with other forms of disabilities are at even greater risk. Specifically, those with developmental, learning, and psychiatric disabilities, which are more likely to be associated with cognitive impairments, experience more sexual assault than people with physical disabilities (Alriksson-Schmidt et al., 2010; Turner, Vanderminden, Finklehor, Hamby, & Shattuck, 2011). This aligns with social workers' tendency to focus on people with emotional and intellectual disabilities in their conversations with us; in fact, when social workers discussed people with physical disabilities, they typically characterized them as having otherwise normative cognition and desires.

People with physical disabilities without cognitive impairments, such as intellectual disabilities, will have similar understandings of romantic relationships as their typical peers, yet may need support finding romantic partners and counseling to bolster self-esteem that may be affected by relationship rejection (Azzopardi-Lane & Callus, 2015). People with cognitive disabilities may be more likely to easily engage in romantic relationships, yet need support in understanding the implications of the relationships.

The social workers we interviewed feel that self-esteem challenges among teenagers with disabilities sometimes led them to cope by using drugs and alcohol. This, in turn, decreased their ability to make healthy decisions in the moment (for example, by decreasing assertiveness) and increased their risk for unwanted sexual interaction:

> And sometimes the use of drugs and alcohol to self-medicate. For the disability. And so then therefore, they find themselves in sexual situations. And then they turn into . . . where maybe they don't have the self-esteem to say no. They don't have the decision-making process.

Furthermore, and according to the social workers interviewed, alcohol and drugs may serve as a form of self-medication not only to cope with a psychiatric disability but also for some to cope with past experiences of sexual victimization. Social workers' perspectives were consistent with the trauma-informed service model, which integrates both past trauma and substance use into therapy or case management (Elliot, Bjelajac, Fallot, Markoff, & Reed, 2005). This model can be used by social workers with clients with disabilities who have both past trauma and substance abuse issues. A trauma-informed approach also centralizes healthy relationships as part of the intervention process (Purvis, Cross, & Pennings, 2009).

While people with disabilities are typically referred to as the victims of dating and sexual assault, they are also described as perpetrators to one another or others. This is often a result of being unable to decipher appropriate behaviors or to exert self-control. Sometimes the behavior could be seen as simply inappropriate and a result of the person not fully understanding the implications of his or her behavior. A social worker shares an example of a child with intellectual disability putting his hand down his pants, playing with his penis, then taking his hand out and wiping it on another kid's face. Another example is an adult male with autism spectrum disorder who regularly grabbed women's breasts. Although behaviors such as these may be done by people with disabilities only to aggravate another person or get someone's attention, they can lead to legal issues, such as registered sex offenses, which are prevalent among people with disabilities (Lindsay, Steptoe, & Haut, 2012). There is a link between offenders of sex crimes and previous sexual abuse among people with disabilities (Lindsay et al., 2012).

Social workers can be victims or indirectly affected by such behaviors:

> Today, one of my boys came in and wanted to use the phone. While he was leaving a message, he said, "I want a blow job." I said, "Do not talk like that in front of me. That is offensive." He was so angry that a female would stop him. I don't know if any female has ever said, "That's offensive."

This social worker demonstrates setting boundaries, which is especially important when working with people with disabilities. Furthermore, curricula that model appropriate versus inappropriate demonstrations of affection, such as those offered by the Dibble Institute (for example, Mike's Crush; Mitelman & Von Kohorn, 2012), may be used to teach healthy and appropriate ways to engage in romantic or sexual displays of affection.

Dyadic Level: Romantic and Sexual Relationships

The sexual relationships of people with disabilities generally take place in the extreme ends of the spectrum of sexual possibilities. People with disabilities are two times more likely to have their first sexual experiences in uncommitted sexual contexts (that is, with a stranger) and two and a half times more likely to engage in sexual relationships in highly committed contexts (that is, marriage) compared with people without disabilities (Shandra & Chowdhury, 2012). In contrast, first sexual experiences for a majority of people without disabilities occur while they are in romantic relationships, which tend to be in the middle of the spectrum as they are neither uncommitted nor married (Martinez, Copen, & Abma, 2011). We discuss these dynamics in greater depth below, as well as in chapters 7 and 8.

Person in a Peer Environment

People with disabilities, and particularly youths, may feel added pressure to exert their sexuality in an attempt to appear normal (Greydanus & Omar, 2008) or to hide a less noticeable disability (Shandra & Chowdhury, 2012). Adolescents may not be as skilled at communicating their needs and desires, a risk that is exacerbated in youths with disabilities but not dissimilar from youths without disabilities (Williams & Adams, 2013b). Regardless, such contexts blur the lines between "casual" sex and victimization for people with disabilities and call attention to developmental considerations (that is, happening for people with disabilities across the lifespan). Amid peer norms that perpetuate casual sex in the context of partying, drug and alcohol use heighten sexual risk taking for youths without disabilities (Williams & Adams, 2013a) and reflect added risk for youths with disabilities as they attempt to fit in. A school social worker notes that students with disabilities had been date-raped. Again, this highlights the relationship between victimization and substance use. In this case, substance abuse adds to the vulnerability of people with disabilities.

People with disabilities, just like those without, are tasked with forming their own identity within a social world. For individuals without disabilities, this task happens in adolescence; for individuals with disabilities, this task may span various times in one's life, and facets (for example, sexual desire, puberty, relationship formation) may occur asynchronously. We now know that the development of romantic and sexual relationships is fundamental to individual identity development (Beyers & Seiffge-Krenke, 2010). Social workers commonly refer to relationship misunderstandings, such as assuming mutual sexual or relationship intentions, which complicate the development of relationships but are not unique to people with disabilities. For example, among a sample of Mexican American and European American adolescents (ages 15–17), we found that a peer culture perpetuating hookups and "friends with benefits" relationships resulted in relationship misunderstandings. Girls were particularly vulnerable to participating in these relationships in hopes of securing greater levels of commitment (Williams & Adams, 2013a, 2013b). It follows that the normative desire of people with disabilities for intimate relationships may put them at heightened risk for doing what they perceive as normal within their peer culture:

> A kid who had intellectual disability was given the message that he should be a gangster. That is what he believed he should be to hook up with girls. And because he doesn't have the cognitive abilities, he takes on that persona that he should be a gangster.

The above example underscores the importance of situating disability and severity in the context of a normative quest to secure identity while also holding meaningful relationships with peers and romantic relationship partners (Blatt & Blass, 1996). It also highlights the influence of peer and media culture as perpetrating what may be considered normal or popular.

Person in a Family and Social Work Environment

Social workers are tasked with complex roles that require both advocacy and protection of vulnerable populations. Serving as an advocate for the romantic relationship needs of people with disabilities is challenging, particularly when they have already been victimized. Furthermore, social workers navigate the mesosystem, including family or legal guardians, which may be at odds with the sexual health needs of clients. For example, guardians of people with disabilities sometimes request 24-hour supervision to protect the clients from victimization, yet this may also limit opportunities to develop romantic relationships, as discussed more in chapter 8. Such well-intentioned restrictions may compromise the sexual and romantic expression of clients, who lack a voice to advocate for their own desires. Residential supportive service staff and families of people with intellectual disabilities are often in disagreement over how much freedom clients should be given to pursue these relationships. In one study, support staff (42 percent; $n = 153$) were more likely than family members (10 percent; $n = 155$) to believe that clients should have privacy to engage in intimate or sexual relationships (Evans, McGuire, Healy, & Carley, 2009). Interviews with people with intellectual disabilities receiving residential supportive services found that, overall, they felt restricted by rules pertaining to their ability to have privacy with a boyfriend or girlfriend (Healy, McGuire, Evans, & Carley, 2009).

Among adolescents, social workers voice the belief that parents often played a role in restricting their child with a disability. Mothers of adolescents with disabilities have reported purposefully refraining from talking with their children about sex even though they had concerns about their sexual vulnerability (Pownall et al., 2012). Although some parents may not discuss sex with children with disabilities, because they believe that they will not understand, others may feel that talking to their child about sex may introduce or encourage it and fear that their child will be victimized or will victimize someone else.

Although social workers feel that some families were indeed concerned about the sexual health of their children, they also told stories of students who did not receive support from their family when they divulged incidences of interpersonal abuse. Sometimes this resulted in self-blame: one social worker describes an adolescent on her caseload who reported that she brought the abuse on herself. These types of responses to the abuse, including a lack of support, reflect larger and interrelated systemic challenges. Social workers may be the first (and sometimes only) source to offer help, according to interviewed social workers. Furthermore, it is not unusual for social workers to support clients whose families are not available or involved in their lives; therefore, their support system may consist primarily of paid professionals' and peers' support.

MACROSYSTEM

The macrosystem, described by Bronfenbrenner as cultural "blueprints" (1977, 1979), affects people with disabilities and includes their increased vulnerability to experiences of sexual and other forms of dating violence victimization. Social workers express difficulty "combating culture." This includes media portrayals of unhealthy relationships and larger cultural contexts of violent communities, poor economic conditions, and an overall lack of supportive services. Social workers observe that their clients often come from homes where violence, abuse, substance abuse, or gang activity is present. Social workers support clients in urban areas, many of whom have experienced poverty; positive role models are essential to developing healthy relationships but may be difficult to find in impoverished areas (McBride Murry, Berkel, Gaylord-Harden, Copeland-Linder, & Nation, 2011). Even though social workers intervene with clients, they often feel as though after they leave, their messages are lost, because their clients return to environments that do not support their messages. Here we discuss media and cultural considerations that are salient to the social workers interviewed. We end with discussion of historical victimization and cultural messages, both of which are historically embedded macro-contexts experienced among many youths with disabilities. These historical and cultural mores are perhaps the most troubling vulnerabilities according to social workers, who feel that cycles of violence often carried forward into the types of relationship dynamics individuals with disabilities enacted in their current relationships. In essence, discussing macro-systemic vulnerability brings us full circle to an individual within his or her romantic relationships—including a social worker's role in working to maximize relationship health.

Media

Although portrayals of romantic relationships and sexuality in the media affect most people, people with disabilities may be especially in tune to media messages because they are not typically represented in sexual roles (Tepper, 2000; Wiegerink, Roebroeck, Donkervoort, Stam, & Cohen-Kettenis, 2006). One social worker makes a connection between media, vulnerability, and victimization:

> What they see on TV, reality TV . . . the whole show is about them
> having sex with people, like hooking up with different people, drink-
> ing, partying, and going out [to] bars and stuff. That kind of stuff is
> so prevalent . . . and so guys would pressure them into giving them
> [a] blow job and saying "Well, it's not really sex."

Because little education is provided through school systems or organizations for people with disabilities, they may have a poor understanding of their own sexual bodies (Swango-Wilson, 2011). The fact that the bodies of people with disabilities may be different from those of others may also exacerbate this. People with physical disabilities, developmental disabilities, or those on certain medications sometimes experience either delayed or early pubertal development, difficulty with menses, and physical impairments that could affect their sexual functions (Greydanus & Omar, 2008; Grover, 2011). Internalization of sexual stigma may promote sexual risk taking among people with disabilities (Shandra & Chowdhury, 2012).

We found in our research that even adolescents without disabilities had difficulty distinguishing between media messages and real life (Rueda, Nagoshi, & Williams, 2014). This idealistic notion of romantic relationship involvement is characteristic of adolescents' first romantic experiences (Larson, Clore, & Wood, 1999). However, as another social worker explains, this desire to be loved can lead people with disabilities to engage in unwanted sexual behaviors: "They're more vulnerable to coercion, and manipulation, and believing, 'He loves me, he's going to stay with me, it's okay to do this [have sex].'"

Culture

Ethnic cultures also sometimes exacerbate vulnerability among people with disabilities. For example, a social worker observes that in Hispanic culture, "Boys are prized and first-born sons get away with murder and girls are pretty much on the bottom until they become mothers—then they jump up the pecking order." Traditional Hispanic culture often values *machismo*, which is associated with positive attributes (for example, chivalry) and negative attributes (for example, domination of women). It is also associated with a corresponding role that values women as caretakers of the home and family (Gonzalez-Guarda, Vermeesch, Florom-Smith, McCabe, & Peragallo, 2013). Although Hispanics are not a homogenous people and vary in their degree of traditional gendered beliefs, strong family orientation continues to be a priority (Updegraff, Umaña-Taylor, McHale, Wheeler, & Perez-Brena, 2012). Furthermore, people with disabilities, especially girls, may feel pressure to take on traditional roles when faced with additional challenges to obtain further education and employment. Social workers felt that these traditional roles may heighten their vulnerability for dating violence.

The geographic location of our interviews affected the experiences of social workers, many of whom were Hispanic themselves or worked with Hispanic and Native American individuals with disabilities. In the context of cultural norms, some social workers refer to a culture of violence that is sometimes created or sustained in communities in which multiple generations have experienced victimization. The culture of violence the social workers described illustrates an acceptance or fatalism of romantic relationship and sexual violence. Although this phenomenon exists in other communities and among other ethnic groups, American Indians disproportionately experience dating and sexual violence (Crossland, Palmer, & Brooks, 2013; Rutman, Taualii, Ned, & Tetrick, 2012). A social worker observes that acceptance of abusive relationships appeared to be intensified among clients who lived on reservations. Research has found that Native American women who live on reservations are more likely than other Native American women to experience abuse and injuries as a result of abuse (Crossland et al., 2013; Linton, 2015).

Past Victimization and the Cycle of Abuse

Risk factors for sexual victimization are additive and may be thought of as embedded within overlapping and mutually influencing contexts. Individual vulnerabilities (for example, poor self-esteem) are influenced by media and peer messages that define what is sexually attractive. Furthermore, and as demonstrated, cultural contexts shape norms for what may be considered "okay" versus "a big deal." Historical contexts, including those experiences that the individual with a disability brings into a relationship, also shape one's likelihood to perpetrate or be victimized by sexual or other forms of intimate partner violence. For example, it was not uncommon for social workers' clients to have experienced past sex abuse from family members or older people. Research shows that children with disabilities who have single parents, stepparents, or nonparent caregivers are more than twice as likely to experience sexual or other forms of victimization by a family member (Turner et al., 2011). Once victimized, individuals are more likely to be revictimized and to victimize others in future relationships; this is commonly referred to as the cycle of abuse.

In addition to sexual violence, emotional or verbal violence (for example, putting someone down, name calling), physical violence (for example, throwing objects, hitting), and relational violence (for example, spreading rumors about someone or harming another's reputation) are other forms of violence that many adolescents experience, including those without disabilities (Williams, 2014). In addition, men and women with disabilities are more likely to experience intimate partner violence (Hahn, McCormick, Silverman, Robinson, & Koenen, 2014), with women being particularly vulnerable to severe forms (Brownridge, 2006). In our interviews, one high school social worker describes instances of name calling, such as "bitch" or "ho," within the romantic relationships of some of her clients and described this as a precursor to other forms of violence. Some social workers have witnessed examples of emotional abuse in which one partner was controlling the other; for example, youths with disabilities would inform each other whom they could befriend. Indeed, social workers reflect on multiple types of abuse, ranging from verbal and psychological to physical. The consequences of the following scenario were both physical and psychological: "I've seen kids where they take the girl's hands . . . and twist their wrists and scream at them in their face. I've seen a girl slap a boy, because she was upset with him." Psychological abuse is often hidden, however, and often difficult for social workers to identify. Research of Hispanic and African American adolescents with disabilities found, however, that significantly more adolescents self-reported psychological (66 percent) than physical (35 percent) victimization (Alleyne-Green, Coleman-Cowger, & Henry, 2012). In some cases, the physical abuse that some social workers encountered was extreme, including the following with a Native American adolescent in a clinical practice setting:

> When she came in last week crying and discussing how he [her boyfriend] tried to choke her to death. I said to her once she was crying, "Did he do that to you?" She said yes. You think about it, that's her life. She's pregnant, on crutches, he tried to choke her.

As these examples demonstrate, clients may report the abuse to social workers, particularly because others, such as peers, may minimize their experiences.

IMPLICATIONS FOR SOCIAL WORK PRACTICE

Social workers recommend individual and psychoeducational therapeutic support for people with disabilities to prevent vulnerability and address victimization. Individual therapy should address past trauma, help the client to establish boundaries, and finally work to promote self-esteem and self-advocacy skills. Because substance abuse and trauma are often connected, interventions should be integrated to address both needs simultaneously using trauma-informed care (Elliot et al., 2005). Together with the disability, trauma often creates a diminished sense of self-worth. A social worker explains that self-esteem needs to be addressed in people with disabilities who display promiscuous behavior or have experienced victimization. Another school social worker suggests that to prevent victimization, we need to address self-esteem early before it starts to plummet, usually between ages nine and 12. Puberty, which is associated with changes in self-esteem, tends to occur among children during this time (Morin, Maïano, Marsh, Janosz, & Nagengast, 2011), yet the pubertal development of people with disabilities may differ. Also, adolescents of racial and ethnic minorities may be more likely than whites to experience a decrease in self-esteem during puberty (Morin et al., 2011). Social workers also suggest teaching students self-advocacy skills, which include the general ability to advocate for disability services and human rights but can also include the ability to be assertive in relationships. This social worker refers to self-advocacy and rights training for people with intellectual disabilities:

> Just educating them, letting them know that this is illegal. People with disability, they get "rights" training and they know their twenty-four rights. . . . A lot of it is just remembering and processing and retaining information. They may remember that exploitation is wrong, and they may remember that one month, but then they'll forget it the next month, so just the repetition in trying to help advocate for them and help them . . . teach them to advocate for themselves. That's the biggest thing.

Social workers also acknowledge that self-advocacy should be taught after self-esteem has been addressed, because youths need to have confidence before they are able to stand up for themselves.

Psychoeducational groups adapted to meet the needs of people with disabilities can also be used to teach about healthy relationships and the cycle of violence. People with disabilities should be encouraged to obtain these services in the least restrictive environment possible and with their typical peers if possible. This inclusion model is prioritized according to IDEA (2004). However, if separate and adapted services are necessary for people with disabilities, such as those with moderate or severe cognitive impairments, then services should be tailored to meet the developmental needs of clients. Social workers suggest having guest speakers or group members share their victimization or vulnerability experiences in small groups. Another common tool includes role playing or watching videos and identifying appropriate and inappropriate behaviors pertaining to romantic relationships (Mitelman & Von Kohorn, 2012). People with autism spectrum disorder and other social communication disorders may also benefit from the use of asynchronous activities, such as Internet discussion boards, which may limit the discomfort experienced in social interactions.

CONCLUSION

Disability places an individual at risk of possible sexual victimization, particularly when the individual is embedded within additive risk factors within his or her environment. Social workers identify some of the intrapersonal processes, such as self-esteem and decision-making skills, which can be improved through preventive efforts, including individual and group therapy. Social workers believe that interventions should be ordered as follows: (a) address trauma stemming from previous sexual victimization; (b) improve self-esteem; (c) enhance self-advocacy skills; and (d) provide psychoeducation on healthy relationships and the cycle of violence. Exosystemic and macrosystemic influences, such as community and culture, can be protective or exacerbate sexual and other forms of vulnerability among people with disabilities. Social workers have an opportunity to influence these systems by bringing additional resources to impoverished communities and encouraging positive aspects of one's culture.

7

Pregnancy and Parenting

Social workers share many stories of clients who became pregnant and some who parented children. Clients' attitudes toward pregnancy and parenting were influenced by peer and cultural subjective norms pertaining to contraception use: some lacked perceived behavioral control to advocate for themselves in using contraception; some also desired pregnancy. For one or more of these reasons, pregnancy and parenting were common among the adolescents and adults with disabilities served by the social workers. People with disabilities are just as likely as others to experience pregnancy, yet are more likely to become pregnant as teenagers and while single than people without disabilities, which demonstrates vulnerabilities among people with disabilities and the need for supportive services (Höglund, Lindgren, & Larsson, 2012; Shandra, 2011; Wiegerink et al., 2006). Although the experiences of clients with disabilities represent mesosystemic and macrosystemic influences, the attitudes, intentions, subjective norms, and perceived behavioral control toward pregnancy and parenting are also consistent with the theory of planned behavior (Ajzen, 1991; Bronfenbrenner, 1979). Attitudes are an individual's positive or negative feelings toward a behavior. Intentions refer to the degree to which a person has a favorable intent toward using contraception or experiencing pregnancy or parenting. Perceived norms are apparent social pressures to either avoid contraception or experience pregnancy or parenting. Perceived behavioral control refers to the ease or difficulty for clients to avoid or experience pregnancy or parenting (Ajzen, 1991). Other influences widely discussed by social workers were adolescents' understanding of consequences regarding pregnancy, the influence of medications (including withdrawal from medication usage) on sexual contexts and on the pregnancy itself, and organizational policies that influenced the ability to intervene.

MICROSYSTEM

Individual: Understanding Consequences

Some adolescents and adults with disabilities lack overall understanding of the anatomy and function of their bodies. A social worker reports that an African American male client with schizophrenia and bipolar disorder asked him, "Why am I having wet dreams?" The social worker explained to him,

> "Because your body has to dispose of the sperm . . . your sperm dies and so your body is naturally getting rid of that if you're not masturbating." Masturbating is a healthy thing, and he can't see that because his culture does not permit that.

Social workers report that it may not always be obvious which clients struggle with these misunderstandings. A social worker described a client of hers who had been sexually active for a while before getting pregnant. Although it was not obvious that this client had an intellectual disability, she did lack an understanding of her body. People with disabilities may not be taught about their bodies early enough. Adults with visual impairments have recommended that general education on biology, anatomy, and pubertal changes occur at an age before they experience puberty (Wild, Kelly, Blackburn, & Ryan, 2014). As discussed in chapter 5, even when children with disabilities are exposed to sex education content (for example, videos on their sexual anatomy and puberty), they may not understand it or may be left out of classroom discussion. Beyond understanding the biology and anatomy of one's own body, social workers often feel that their clients with disabilities do not recognize the consequences of sex. Social workers express that some of their clients "think [pregnancy is] from French kissing" or "holding hands." This lack of understanding supports research among physicians finding that they often do not provide sexual health information to people with disabilities because they are concerned that their patients cannot make informed decisions about sex (Blum et al., 1991; McCarthy, 2009). This social worker shares an example of adolescents with mental illnesses:

> We have two kids who are both [disabled], one more than the other, but the boy is very mentally ill. I mean very mentally ill. They got pregnant and she had a miscarriage and they were pregnant again within like a month.

However, the decision to have sex without the use of contraception is complex and embedded within not only one's ability to understand consequences but also attitudes and intentions to become pregnant.

Given a lack of sexual health education or of appropriately tailored sexual health content, as discussed in chapter 5, people with disabilities may not understand contraception use (Galea, Butler, Iacono, & Leighton, 2004). A study of high-functioning women with intellectual disabilities found that more than about half of the sample did not have any knowledge about contraception or reproduction (McCarthy, 2009). Social workers also note that most adolescents and adults with disabilities were receiving informal education about their bodies and contraception use mostly from their peers, a finding that is consistent with previous research on adults with visual impairments (Wild et al., 2014). This worried social workers because of the large amount of misinformation available on the Internet or from peers.

Attitudes and Intention

The way that people with disabilities feel about contraception and pregnancy is quite varied, and some of that depends on their age. It is common for social workers to say that adolescents hold neutral attitudes toward pregnancy and parenting, which lessened their intention to use contraception. Adolescents with disabilities whose parents experienced teenage pregnancy were more likely than others to accept teenage pregnancy as a way of life. One social worker explains it as fatalistic. Social workers mention that condoms and other forms of contraception were sometimes perceived negatively. One social worker believes that her adolescent clients with disabilities are playing Russian roulette because they rarely use contraception. Furthermore, we know from research that adolescents' decisions to use contraception are influenced by their partner's attitudes and that male adolescents' attitudes have more impact on whether the couple will use contraceptives (Vasilenko, Kreager, & Lefkowitz, 2015).

Although most of the social workers described this fatalistic attitude among their clients, others observed that some girls and boys have a clear intention to have sex that results in pregnancy. Generally, social workers view clients with disabilities as seeking more acceptance within themselves and among their peers and families. A social worker explains that adolescent girls with disabilities saw pregnancy as a change of identity from someone with a disability to someone who was going to have a baby: "I have this cute baby in me and [they] kinda fantasize about maybe what that role is gonna be." Together with other factors (for example, family seems more viable than career ambitions), this helps to contextualize why adolescents with disabilities are significantly more likely than those without disabilities to want a pregnancy during their first experience of sexual intercourse (Shandra & Chowdhury, 2012).

Social workers discussed how some families and cultures, especially Hispanic cultures, associate pregnancy and parenting with respect. Hispanic cultures tend to prioritize parenthood and raising children, yet discussions of contraception are often taboo (Milbrath, Ohlson, & Eyre, 2009). Some social workers hold the view that the family's positive perception of parenthood influenced not only girls but also adolescent boys to have thoughts such as the following: "impregnate as many girls as possible and that makes you a man." Social workers observe that adults with disabilities perceive pregnancy and parenting as common life experiences. Social workers also serve adults with intellectual disabilities and psychiatric disorders, such as veterans, who had children as a result of family planning.

Subjective Norms

Peers and family influence norms held by people with disabilities about pregnancy and parenting. According to social workers, adolescents and adults talk to their peers about sex, yet discussions of contraceptive use were not a major part of conversations or were discussed in a negative light and looked down upon.

Adolescents and adults with disabilities who were dependent on their family for support, such as those with severe or moderate forms of intellectual disabilities or those having autism spectrum disorder, were particularly influenced by their family's norms. Social workers reported that "most families are really protective." This is a common research finding; mothers of adolescents with disabilities refrained from talking to their children about sex or contraceptives even if they were suspicious that their child may be vulnerable to sexual coercion (Pownall et al., 2012). Social workers take a different approach and advocate for their clients to receive gynecological care. Yet, in doing so, they reported running into barriers from protective families. A social worker shares an example of a conversation with a parent of a child with a severe intellectual disability:

> You going to take them to the OB-GYN? . . . and they're like . . . , "Not my daughter. She has a disability." "Just because she has a disability doesn't mean she doesn't have human urges. . . ." "My child is disabled, she doesn't participate . . . she doesn't masturbate or do any of this."

The lack of support among families of adolescents and adults with disabilities in obtaining that care may be contributing to the fact that women with disabilities are less likely than their peers to have their gynecological health care needs met (Servais, 2006). Furthermore, studies have found that ethnic-minority families (served by many of our social workers) face economic and social challenges that contribute to a lack of sexual health awareness; for example, they are less likely to be able to access clinics close by, which ultimately contributes to the use of less optimal forms of contraceptives (for example, condoms) over more optimal methods (for example, IUDs; see Haider, Stoffel, Donenberg, & Geller, 2013).

Perceived Behavioral Control

Social workers are concerned about their clients' lack of perceived control in making decisions pertaining to preventing pregnancy. Social workers often shared examples that demonstrated their clients' inability to advocate for themselves. A social worker reported,

> I have a lot of women who have been coerced into having sex with their partners. Or for instance, they have a history of sexual abuse and they have a stable partner for a couple of years, but they don't like having sex. But they don't feel comfortable enough communicating that to their partner because they feel they'll push them away.

Another social worker who supports adolescents observes that girls with and without disabilities are typically not communicating with their partners about using contraception. Social workers also mention that boys and men did not seem to take responsibility for condom or contraceptive use; however, there was a bias among social workers to place responsibility on girls or women to initiate prevention. This is consistent with the feminist belief that there has been a silencing of female sexual desire and use of women are gatekeepers for sex and contraception (Fine, 1988). A study of women with intellectual disabilities found that they rarely expected sexual desire and acceded to pleasureless sexual acts in a belief that this was their role. Their use of contraception to prevent pregnancy was often controlled by family members or staff (Fitzgerald & Withers, 2013).

Drugs, Alcohol, and Medications

The use of drugs, alcohol, and medications complicated preventing pregnancy and experiencing pregnancy among people with disabilities. A social worker serving adolescents with mental illnesses reports that they often self-medicated with drugs and alcohol and then found themselves in sexual situations in which they did not have the decision-making skills or self-esteem to say "no." In addition, if a person with a disability experienced pregnancy, she was not always able to take her usual medication and experienced erratic behavior or the symptoms that the medication would typically address. A social worker serving adolescent girls expresses just how much this complicated the situation: "They're dealing not only with hormones of being a teenager, having a disability, not being able to manage their behaviors or thoughts or feelings, and the hormones of pregnancy."

MACROSYSTEM
Subjective Norms

Social work interventions and policies sometimes create barriers for social workers. Social work services regarding the rights of birth mothers with disabilities have changed over time. One social worker, reflecting on her career, reports that 25 years ago, social workers automatically terminated the parental rights of pregnant mothers with disabilities. This social worker was referring to common practice versus a formal policy. Social workers may see the consequences of such actions in clients they serve who may have had their parental rights terminated. However, social workers who serve adolescents and adults with disabilities also note that there seems to be an increased number of people with disabilities who are bearing children; this prompted a more supportive social work response to pregnancies over time. Social workers acknowledge that people with disabilities can be effective caregivers to their children with supports in housing, health care, finances, and grocery shopping, suggesting that current social work services are more supportive of people with disabilities who want to parent a child than services were decades ago.

Social workers also describe the increased difficulties faced by individuals with disabilities who decide to parent, especially among those who are teenagers. A high school social worker reports that the school has an issue—each year about 15 kids who get pregnant do not return to school after having children. Social workers who serve both adolescents and adults report that they often see clients with multiple unplanned pregnancies, which typically results in the children going to foster care, being adopted, or being raised by a family member. Kerr (2000) argues that the belief that people with disabilities should not reproduce continues today, and rather than work with the individual when possible to provide support, these placements may evidence this sentiment. In addition, research shows that the historical practice of sterilization, typically by tubal ligation, of people with disabilities continues in current forms of forced birth control use among people with severe and moderate disabilities, those with guardians, and those living in institutionalized housing, such as group homes (Tilley, Walmsley, Earle, & Atkinson, 2012).

School social workers and those working in adult services also have to be conscious of the policies related to pregnancy and parenting. For example, school social workers working in school districts with abstinence-only education are not legally able to discuss pregnancy prevention with students; if they found out that a student was pregnant, they "have to notify their parents within 24 hours." In addition, those that served adults who live in group homes had to be aware that many group homes do not allow adults with children.

IMPLICATIONS FOR SOCIAL WORK PRACTICE

Social workers often feel as though they are the only ones that adolescents and adults are turning to in discussions pertaining to pregnancy and parenting. Social workers should strive to have an open door policy as much as possible. However, because of policy limitations as discussed in chapter 5, many school social workers discussed having conversations behind closed doors. To allow all social workers to feel comfortable offering pregnancy and parenting counseling and resources, social workers should work for policy change. One school social worker succinctly reiterated this desire:

> If I had my way, I would have a big fishbowl with condoms next to the thing of lollipops, saying "Please take one of each," but you can't do that in a public school, unfortunately you can't do it, it's not allowed. You can't distribute contraception devices on campus.

Few social workers report taking steps to advocate on behalf of policy changes. Furthermore, a strengths framework should be encouraged in social work that recognizes the desire for many youths with disabilities to have family-oriented goals (Shandra, 2011; Shandra & Chowdhury, 2012).

Support services, including those related to pregnancy and parenting, need to be adapted to meet the unique needs of people with disabilities. Research shows that these services, especially health care related to pre-natal care and pregnancy, are not adapted, which causes barriers to care for people with disabilities (Wolowicz-Ruszkowska, 2015). Social workers may act as mediators between their clients and support services or health care professionals by communicating with professionals about the unique needs of their clients.

CONCLUSION

People with disabilities are more likely to desire pregnancy resulting from their first experience of sexual intercourse, to become pregnant as teen-agers, and to be single during pregnancy (Höglund et al., 2012; Shandra & Chowdhury, 2012). According to the social workers we interviewed, individuals' desire to become pregnant may be motivated by their desire to identify as someone other than a person with a disability. They are also more likely to see themselves as unable to pursue career-related ambi-tions and rather to aspire to and follow through with family-oriented goals (Shandra, 2011; Shandra & Chowdhury, 2012). A review of literature com-paring parents with intellectual disabilities to those without found that (a) mothers with intellectual disabilities experienced more risk factors and health issues during pregnancy, (b) parents with intellectual disabilities experience worse health issues, (c) child protection proceedings occurred more for parents with intellectual disabilities, and (d) children of par-ents with intellectual disabilities were more likely to be placed in child protective custody (Llewellyn & Hindmarsh, 2015). Because of assump-tions that they are asexual or at too high a risk to discuss (and supposedly encourage) sexual behavior (Blum et al., 1991; Shandra & Chowdhury, 2012), people with disabilities may fall through the cracks where typi-cally developing adolescents may receive multiple sources of potential influence (that is, from parents, doctors, and schools). Social workers can (a) be available for active listening and counseling, (b) advocate for policy changes to foster more opportunities to educate and support adolescents and adults with disabilities who experience pregnancy and parenting, and (c) mediate the relationship between clients and health care or other professionals to ensure adapted services for people with disabilities.

8

Cohabitation and Marriage

Social workers proudly support people with disabilities to have the choice to cohabitate or celebrate commitment with their intimate partners. Many of the social workers' clients lived happily with an intimate partner or spouse. There was a strong desire among many of the social workers' clients to commit to one person and marry. This is consistent with other research that has found that people with disabilities are just as likely as anyone else to desire companionship and marriage (Bates, Terry, & Popple, 2016; Wells et al., 2003). A qualitative study of people with intellectual disability reported that having a partner and ultimately a ring and marriage ceremony were of great significance and possibly an outward symbol to others of status that they were "just like other people" (Bates et al., 2016, p. 7). However, a desire for marriage does not ultimately determine that it will happen. Another study found that people with disabilities were less likely to fulfill their desires of marriage than their nondisabled counterparts (Janus, 2009).

Taking the step to marry is complicated for many people with disabilities. Cohabitation or marriage potential for people with disabilities who receive professional social work services, government benefits, and assisted living is highly controlled by macrosystemic influences. Benefits issues and policies often prevented companions from living out their days together in the same home or marrying and resulted in intimate partners living in separate places and celebrating their love in commitment ceremonies rather than marriage.

MICROSYSTEM

Social workers want to protect people with disabilities from victimization. This is a realistic concern because victimization is common among people with disabilities (as described in chapter 6). The idea of cohabitation among two people with physical disabilities sparked a social worker's urge to protect them:

> We had one couple that were both in wheelchairs in a handicap accessible apartment and I have to tell you . . . that's a really scary thing. To have two individuals who use power wheelchairs in the community and they would go out. You're just scared for them, because somebody is going to hurt them. However, they were fearless. They got in their power chairs and went to the malls, they went out to eat and . . . nothing had happened to them but it's really hard to let go of that. Like, I want them in a protected environment. But they were very happy and we had staff in there. The guy was able to actually transfer from his chair, but you always think, like, my gosh, if there's a fire, you know, how is he going to get out on time? But that's what they wanted. They lived together.

This quote illustrates the social worker's struggle with an ethical dilemma to protect her clients' well-being while supporting their self-determination (NASW, 2015a).

In cases where the clients had more severe cognitive or physical impairment and a legal guardian, social workers also leaned toward protecting clients' well-being over their self-determination. When adults with disabilities had legal guardians, it was often difficult for them to date enough to get to a place in which they were ready to cohabitate or marry because of constant supervision by support staff. Individuals with legal guardians often lived in supported living arrangements, which had 24-hour staff supervision. Staff supervised all visits with guests in the home, including intimate partner visits. A social worker offers one such example:

> The girl would come over to his house, he might cook supper for them and . . . well staff is typically there . . . they get together for recreational purposes, if they go to a dance, bowling or Special Olympics, something to that end. But seldom do I see them actually consummate a relationship.

MACROSYSTEM
Benefits

Adults with chronic disabilities qualify for many government programs, including but not limited to cash assistance programs (Social Security, Social Security Disability Insurance, and Supplemental Security Income [SSI]), health insurance programs (Medicaid and Medicare), and in-kind resources (food stamps and rental assistance). The most common are SSI, Medicaid, rental assistance, and food stamps. Many people with disabilities live off these four resources and may work jobs that pay them below minimum wage, which is legal according to the Fair Labor Standards section 14(c), to ensure their income stays low enough to continue to qualify for their benefits. All four of these programs include income as a part of the eligibility standards. People with disabilities often fear losing their critical governmental benefits when they consider getting married. In one case, a client's legal guardian feared the loss of her son's benefits:

> His diagnosis was obsessive compulsive disorder, and they both wanted to get married. . . . And the legal guardian was adamantly against them getting married. So often they'll have what we call a "ceremony of commitment, a commitment ceremony" where they're not actually married because it might affect their Social Security or their Medicaid or something to that effect. And they can still live together. But in this particular case, the guardian was adamantly against it as I mentioned. So that wasn't going to be the end all for them.

The fear of losing benefits is rational and is due to interspousal deeming after two SSI or Medicaid recipients marry. *Interspousal deeming* is when "a spouse's income and resources are immediately added to the beneficiary's" (Fiduccia, 2000, p. 169). Medicaid eligibility is minimally 133 percent of the federal poverty level ($15,654.10 annually) according to the Patient Protection and Affordable Care Act (2010) but may differ by state. If a person's income increases above the eligibility rate, he or she will lose Medicaid benefits. The maximum SSI benefit a single individual can receive is $733 per month. That amount is reduced on the basis of other countable income. For example, if a single individual's countable income is $116, then the person would receive only $617 per month from SSI. Once two people who are both eligible for SSI marry, they are treated as a couple. Marriage alone limits how much they will receive from SSI. The maximum SSI benefits a married couple can receive is $1,100 per month (Social Security, 2016). Thus, if those individuals were single, they would collectively receive $1,466. The assumption is that the two will share resources, such as a consolidation of household expenses, thus reducing their need for as much cash assistance (Rand, 2015). If two SSI recipients move in together without being legally married, they potentially could receive $366 more, thus providing a financial incentive to remain single. If a person with SSI marries someone who is not eligible for SSI and has an income above the federal poverty level, he or she will most likely lose SSI benefits (Rains, 2005; Social Security, 2016). There is an assumption that the spouse previously eligible for SSI is less dependent on SSI for cash assistance, because the spouse can take care of him or her. This is another disincentive to marry among SSI recipients. The only incentive to marry that SSI recipients have is that there are survivor benefits for widows of those who receive SSI (Rains, 2005).

Not only did social workers report that their clients' legal guardians feared losing benefits if their clients married, but social workers also want to protect their clients' governmental benefits. One explained that Medicaid was especially important because it not only provided health insurance but also paid for direct staff support and case management. Such resources are necessary for many clients with disabilities to help manage their activities of daily living, such as grocery shopping, cooking, cleaning, and paying bills. One social worker admits:

> We would discourage people from getting married, but we told them they could have, like, a ceremony, a civil ceremony . . . because if they were married, their Social Security benefits would be reduced. So let's say you have two individuals who are getting $700 apiece and now have $1,500. If they got married, usually the woman's Social Security would be cut in half. So we would encourage them that if they wanted to get married, they could get married because some people wanted to get married. But we would encourage them to maybe just have a ceremony so they could keep their benefits, and they would be financially better off.

It appeared that many of the interviewed social workers felt that their clients' loss of benefits was worse than not living out their dream of getting married.

Assisted-Living Policies

Many people with disabilities depend on assisted living, which provides housing and support staff. These services are reimbursed by Medicaid's Home and Community Based Services waiver program. People with chronic disabilities who need support staff typically live in group home settings. Although they sometimes have their own room, they share a residence with other people with disabilities and are under staff supervision 24 hours a day. Typically, people who receive group home services do not marry, because group homes rarely provide living arrangements for couples.

Many group home organizations have policies restricting people of opposite gender (including married couples) from living together. One group home reported that "they were not staffed or designed to supervise married couples or assist married couples with the dynamics of their relationships" (Associated Press, 2013). Social workers describe another issue related to group homes supporting married couples. Because group homes are reimbursed by Medicaid, which is paid for by taxes, social workers feel responsible to taxpayers. One government-employed, administrative social worker mentioned that, although she believes that engaging in intimate relationships was important to her clients with intellectual disabilities, if one were to get pregnant while he or she was supposed to be supervised by 24-hour staff in the group home, the state would be liable and responsible. This might upset not only the legal guardian but taxpayers as well. Society's often negative view of marriage and cohabitation among people with disabilities can be a heavy weight on the social worker's shoulders. Social workers attempt to accommodate their clients in group homes within the constraints of policies and society's pressures:

> It would depend. One of the rules that we had is you could not date someone who you lived with. So if we found that someone was romantically involved with somebody in the same group home, we would move one of the people out but they could date.

IMPLICATIONS FOR SOCIAL WORK PRACTICE

Social workers struggle with balancing their ethical responsibilities to promote their clients' well-being and self-determination. For instance, should they support clients to cohabitate or marry when they could possibly lose the government benefits that they are dependent on for housing, food, and medical care? Social workers tend to lean conservatively toward supporting their clients to keep their government benefits and obtain their goals of marriage in other ways, such as through commitment ceremonies. Social workers aim to protect their clients from losing critical benefits, but this protection limits the clients' self-determination.

Social workers' discussion of society's or taxpayers' perspectives is important. In the NASW (2015a) code of ethics, Ethical Standard 1.01, "Commitment to Clients," states that

> social workers' primary responsibility is to promote the well-being of clients. In general, clients' interests are primary. However, social workers' responsibility to the larger society or specific legal obligations may on limited occasions supersede the loyalty owed clients, and clients should be advised.

The example given in the NASW (2015a) code of ethics is regarding potential breach of confidentiality for reporting child abuse. Although that is a very different situation, the larger society does affect social workers' opinions and actions related to cohabitation of adults with intellectual disabilities. Social workers report feeling more responsible to the larger society than to their clients, thus restricting their clients' ability to cohabitate in some cases.

Society's larger perspective on people with disabilities cohabitating and marrying is embedded in policies and laws. Governmental disincentives to marry continue to exist. Marriage penalties among welfare recipients prevent those in poverty from taking advantage of the long-term benefits of marriage that have the potential to raise their standard of living in the long run, such as inheritance benefits, spousal support on separation, and health insurance (Rand, 2015). Marriage disincentives are especially harsh among couples that include a person without a disability and a person with a disability who is eligible for SSI or Medicaid. This is because the person with SSI or Medicaid could potentially lose all his or her benefits. People who received SSI or Medicaid before marriage and later face a divorce, which is higher among people with disabilities than among the general population, will be forced to reapply for their benefits (Singleton, 2012). Research has found that there is a decreasing trend of marriage between people with and without disabilities (Tumin, 2016).

Policies surrounding marriage differ on a global scale, as do attitudes about disability. For example, McKenzie and Swartz (2011) discuss stigma associated with disability in South Africa and how marriage can be seen as a way of destabilizing disability. Marriage is something children with disabilities often grow up hoping for. This can leave them vulnerable to those who may offer false hope of a serious relationship but desire only sex (McKenzie & Swartz, 2011). Furthermore, whereas adults with disabilities in the United States struggle with the choice to face consequences and marry if they want to, those with disabilities in some other countries may face a lack of choice through forced marriage. Although none of the social workers we interviewed discussed forced marriage among their clients, it is a salient issue for people with disabilities globally (Rauf, Saleem,

Clawson, Sanghera, & Marston, 2013). The issue should be explored further for professionals working in global social work.

CONCLUSION

Macrosystemic forces strongly influence social workers to prevent adults with disabilities from marrying and cohabitating; social work advocacy is needed to change group home and welfare policies. Advocacy may need to begin by educating society. The general population may need to learn and accept that adults with disabilities often desire love, marriage, and cohabitation just like anyone else. Social workers should (a) remember their commitment to the client in relation to cohabitation and marriage among people with disabilities and (b) advocate for their clients' right to marriage without sacrificing their entitlements.

9

Intimate Relationships in Older Adulthood

With an aging baby boomer population, approximately 15 percent of the U.S. population is aged 65 years or older. This number is expected to increase to 20 percent by 2025 (Ortman, Velkoff, & Hogan, 2014). As people age, they are more at risk to experience disability; those 85 and older are at a particularly high risk of disability (National Institutes of Health, 2013). Up to one-third of older adults remain sexually active well into their 80s (Schick et al., 2010). However, as the social workers described, family members and health professionals often do not expect older adults with disabilities to have intimate and sexual needs; thus, older adults with disabilities may be especially vulnerable to lacking support to express their intimate and sexual desires. Although one social worker expresses that some older adult clients may be embarrassed to discuss sex and admit that they are sexually active, all other social workers who served older adults with disabilities report that they commonly discuss intimacy and sexuality with their clients. Tang (2014) noted that because aging baby boomers lived through the sexual revolution of the 1960s, their comfort with expressing their sexuality may be higher than it was among previous aging cohorts. Although disability, ability to consent, physical abilities, public perception, and institutional residence may hinder their relationships, the older adults with disabilities served by the social workers we interviewed were engaging in intimate and sexual relationships.

MICROSYSTEM

Individual Level: Desire

Regardless of age or ability, the social workers describe their clients' desire to express sexuality and engage in intimacy and sexual activity. Some clients were single or widowed. One social worker describes her widowed 92-year-old client who always had to buy lipstick: "It's called fiery red. It makes her feel good about herself. She says, 'Yes, I'm old and wrinkly, but yet I still wanna look pretty. I wanna look great, somebody to see me.'" A different social worker describes her single, male client: "He may be 88 and blind and has to wear support stockings, but he would still like to have a woman in his life." Other clients had intimate partners and continued to desire intimacy in their relationships. Research has found that at least half of married people with dementia continue to engage in sex (Dourado, Finamore, Barroso, Santos, & Laks, 2010). The following example illustrates not only the desire for sex but a spouse's creativity to engage in sex regardless of disability:

> Her husband has very profound dementia, but he's still, as [his wife] said with a smile, "very romantic." And she said, "He loves to be romantic and he doesn't like to bathe," so I told him, "If you want romance, you have to take a bath." So she says, "That's how I get him to bathe every day." . . . I think her word "romantic" is a euphemism for "having sex."

Desires may include sexual intimacy with another individual, masturbation, or romantic intimacy with shows of affection (for example, handholding, touch). Desires are affected by societal beliefs about sexuality among older adults, and unfortunately the United States' youth-driven culture tends to stigmatize sex among older adults (Hyde & DeLamater, 2008). Social workers should recognize and value sexual desire in their clients.

Disability

Although many older adults with disabilities do not seem to let their disability hold them back from engaging in intimate and sexual relationships, disability sometimes prevented initiation of relationships. A social worker who served older veterans with visual impairments describes various aspects of how their disability prevented them from initiating relationships:

> Some say that they can't really see people, they can't tell what they look like. . . . And some feel hesitant meeting new people, because they don't want them to know about their impairment, because a lot of them don't look like they have a visual impairment unless they're holding their cane.

Older adults in general often suffer from loneliness (Newall, Chipperfield, Bailis, & Stewart, 2013), and having a disability may exacerbate that experience. Loneliness has also been shown to increase functional disability and is associated with earlier mortality (Perissinotto, Cenzer, & Covinsky, 2012).

Dependency

Some have a dependency on an intimate or sexual relationship to secure their resources, such as housing, finances, or general assistance. A social worker explains that sometimes older adults with disabilities will stay in abusive relationships because their partner is the breadwinner and they fear that they will lose everything. This is a concept referred to as an "economically motivated relationship," which is when a person stays in a relationship longer than he or she wanted because of economic pressures, such as money, a place to live, or services (Cimino, in press; Dunkle, Wingood, Camp, & DiClemente, 2010). The term "elder abuse" is also used to signify that an older adult has been a victim of physical abuse, sexual abuse, neglect, or abandonment. This term also can signify financial exploitation of an older person (U.S. Department of Health and Human Services, 2016).

Ability to Consent

The ability to consent to sex is a major issue for older adults and people with disabilities. Recently, an older adult caregiver–husband was sued for engaging in sex with his spouse with dementia, who was deemed unable to consent to sex by a physician at a residential nursing home (Belluck, 2015). It complicates the issue further that there has been an association found between dementia and hypersexual behavior (Wallace & Safer, 2009). As Tang (2014) explains, U.S. societal attitudes of discomfort with the idea of older adults with cognitive impairments engaging in sexual activity have resulted in a lack of laws or general guidelines on the subject. Thus, professionals in the United States have a lot of discretion in determining who can and cannot consent to sex and how to proceed. This differs from other countries, such as the United Kingdom, which have blanket prohibition of sexual conduct involving people with dementia in institutional living arrangements where the mental capacity of one or both partners is compromised (Bartlett, 2010).

Social workers believe that sometimes cognitive impairment, such as dementia, can prevent someone from having the ability to consent to sex. One social worker describes how she negotiated such a situation:

> If the resident doesn't understand what's going on, I've had to stop it to explain to the spouse that due to her cognitive ability she cannot give the consent for them to be together. That can be hard on the spouse [who] is wanting to be with his wife, but she can't be with her husband because of her cognitive ability.

Another social worker explains that it can also be helpful to have a psychologist there to explain cognitive impairment to the spouse. This social worker also offered other methods of expressing intimacy to the spouse, such as holding hands or kissing.

On another note, social workers mention that just because some of their clients have dementia does not mean that they cannot express their needs and wants. Therefore, the ability to consent depends on a magnitude of cognitive delay. If the client has the ability to consent, social workers recommend that he or she be given privacy to engage in intimacy and sex. Several social workers note that some older couples requested larger hospital beds so they could lie next to one another.

Physical Ability

Among those older adults with disabilities who can consent to and desire sex, some expressed concern over their physical ability to engage in sex. One social worker describes having a client in her 80s who was being courted by a man in his 60s, but the female client feared that she was too old to have sex, so one day she asked her doctor whether she could be sexually intimate. Her doctor told her to go for it. The woman told the social worker that after that she told the man courting her that they should quit messing around and just have sex. She reported that each morning he comes by for a "booty call." Sometimes older adults with disabilities do not get the same response from physicians, and their condition negatively affects their ability to engage in sex. Although libido decreases with age normally, medications to address different disabilities may also decrease libido (Hillman, 2008). Often this became an issue in the context of a relationship:

> I had a gentleman . . . he's married to a younger spouse, a woman, and they were having conflict because she wants to have sex more often, and he just doesn't have the libido. . . . We have to do some education sometimes with the spouses about the medications and how they affect their sexuality.

MESOSYSTEM
Institutional Residence

Institutional living, such as group homes or nursing homes, poses risks for lack of privacy, mobility, and access to medications to increase libido. Similar to staff at group home institutions discussed in chapter 8, staff at institutions for older adults tend to conservatively address intimacy and sexual health needs of older adults with disabilities according to social workers. This is most likely due to liability. Social workers report that if a client expresses a desire for intimacy, privacy has to be prearranged. This includes ensuring that staff do not enter a patient's room during private time with a sexual partner at a nursing home, which "takes the fun out of the spontaneity of it." Social workers report that they often had to educate other health professionals about a client's right to privacy and intimacy to provide clients with private time. Mixed methods research on nursing home staff perceptions of sexuality among older adults with dementia found disagreement between survey responses encouraging sexuality among residents with dementia and focus group discussion about ignoring sexual behaviors (Di Napoli, Breland, & Allen, 2013). This suggests that some health professionals may be supportive or feel like they should be supportive, but it is important to remember that there may be some discomfort with the subject of older adults with disabilities and sexuality. Bauer, Fetherstonhaugh, Tarzia, Nay, and Beattie (2014) developed the Sexuality Assessment Tool to identify how supportive an organization is of all residents' sexual expression. This tool can be used to identify areas of improvement, such as staff perceptions or policies, in institutional residence organizations.

While some older adults with disabilities may have mobility impairments related to their disability, those living in residential facilities often have separate kinds of mobility challenges related to transportation, especially an inability to drive at night. This prevents them from meeting people outside their residence. Social workers report that this often does not hold back older adults with disabilities from expressing their intimate and sexual needs. Some people chose to express their sexual needs through masturbation. One social worker describes an institutional residence that had a policy restricting Viagra prescriptions:

> I also see the physician or psychiatrist prescribe medications like Viagra. Now, it is limited here . . . they're able to get two tablets per month. So some of the times, I have actually said to the psychiatrist, "Why do they need Viagra? They're not in a relationship." And the response I get back is, like, "Uh [name of social worker]?!" And I'm like, "Oh! OK!" So he's basically telling me they're still masturbating.

MACROSYSTEM

Social workers agree that the general public does not perceive intimacy or sexuality as a need among older adults, especially those with disabilities, and is quite judgmental when an older adult with a disability expresses intimacy in public or requests privacy for sexuality. One social worker believes that society's judgment toward the intimacy and sexuality of older adults with disabilities is just related to age. Another explains that it is more due to their disability; society does not believe that people with disabilities should have sex. Two social workers who work in elder protective services describe receiving reports of abuse and neglect for older adults with disabilities because they were seen holding each other's hands or kissing each other. The social workers often found the report to be inappropriate. This is a great example of how a social worker can intervene in a potentially disabling societal structure (the social model of disability; see Oliver, 1996). If the social worker were to investigate potential abuse or neglect because consenting adults with disabilities display affection toward one another, she or he may be contributing to the asexual portrait of people with impairments that society has drawn.

IMPLICATIONS FOR SOCIAL WORK PRACTICE

Social workers recommend being available to discuss, educate, and normalize intimacy and sexual needs with older adult clients with disabilities and their family members. A social worker reports that it can sometimes be challenging to get older adults or their family members to talk about sexuality. Once clients begin to open up about sexual concerns, it is important to listen to them and normalize their experiences:

> I had another client who was telling me that she was quite concerned. . . . She was taking care of her in-laws, and I don't know why she had them in twin beds, but she had them in twin beds in her house and her father-in-law couldn't walk. And every day, every night, he would get out of bed and crawl across the floor to . . . the other bed where his wife was, to get into bed with her and make love to her. And I thought that was very sweet and she was gratified to find out that that was

normal, that it was not an abnormal thing. She thought that, she felt like it was creepy that he wanted to do that . . . she was really relieved to know that her father-in-law was not a pervert.

In addition to normalizing experiences for family members, it is also important to normalize them for the public and care providers.

CONCLUSION

Older adults with disabilities may not have their intimate and sexual needs met because of society's overall perception that they are asexual, given their age and disability. The interviewed social workers reveal that the intimate and sexual lives of their older adult clients with disabilities often improved the quality of their lives. This is consistent with research (Hyde & DeLamater, 2008). In addition, social relationships are associated with increased ability and a longer life (Perissinotto et al., 2012). Social workers should (a) probe about intimate and sexual needs during biopsychosocial assessments with older adult clients with disabilities; (b) educate family members and other professionals about the sexual needs and experiences of older adults with disabilities and normalize these experiences; and (c) establish policies and advocate for laws to protect the rights and safety of older adults with dementia or other cognitive impairments, their family members, and the health professionals supporting them.

10

Overview of the Implications for Social Work Practice

From childhood through older adulthood, people with disabilities experience sexual development, with intimate relationships as a central component. Their ability to participate as sexual citizens is either enabled or disabled by societal practices, structures, and policies. Social workers struggle to fully enable their clients' intimate and sexual health because they work within a system that sometimes prohibits the full sexual citizenship of people with disabilities (for example, on lack of adapted public school sex education, see Stanger-Hall & Hall, 2011; on group home cohabitation policies, see Associated Press, 2013; on social welfare marriage penalties, see Rand, 2015). In addition, they struggle with ethical dilemmas (for example, clients' well-being versus self-determination). Despite these societal challenges, most of the interviewed social workers think outside the box to provide creative, adaptive practices to engage people with disabilities in building self-esteem, learning about sex and intimacy, developing self-advocacy skills, and establishing resources necessary to bear children, cohabitate, or marry if desired.

Self-esteem is key to developing confidence in intimate relationships and avoiding abuse or victimization (Foley et al., 2012). One social worker has children write something good about themselves on sticky notes to boost self-esteem early on. Social workers supporting adolescents and adults express the importance of addressing self-esteem during childhood and preadolescence. Social workers recommend that adolescents and adults with low self-esteem receive individual therapy. Peer groups targeting girls in particular (for example, Girls Circle) can also be effective in developing self-esteem, friendship and relationship skills, social support, body image, and self-efficacy (Hossfeld, 2007; Steese, Dollette, Phillips, & Hossfeld, 2006). There is also now a curriculum available for boys as well (One Circle Foundation, 2012), although social workers would need to adapt these curricula to the youths with disabilities that they serve. The materials are highly adaptable to any particular setting.

Social workers provide age-appropriate sex education accommodating the unique needs of their clients with disabilities. Those who serve youths report starting the conversation early by using creative methods, for example, comic-book strips. They also commonly use books on human sexuality. Adolescents and adults typically receive education on an individual basis or in a group setting. Regardless of the age of the clients served, social workers have open-door policies and encourage their clients to ask them questions regarding sexual and intimate health. However, as discussed in chapters 3 and 7, they often came to serve youths in what were labeled as sexually "problematic" contexts; in other words, youths were referred to them for being "at risk" for sexual behaviors or for associated outcomes (for example, public masturbation, pregnancy) that were concerning to parents or teachers. To include individuals as full sexual citizens, a shift needs to occur whereby social workers and other important figures in the individual's life (for example, parents, teachers) provide proactive and positive sexuality education.

Because people with disabilities are more likely than others to be sexually and otherwise victimized (Baladerian et al., 2013), self-advocacy skills are essential according to social workers. Social workers conduct psychoeducational groups using discussions and guest speakers to teach their clients about healthy relationships, assertiveness, and the cycle of violence. One school social worker facilitates a girls' empowerment group. Friendship building and dating or intimate partner violence prevention programs may be particularly beneficial for youths and adults with disabilities. Some programs developed for youths (for example, Mike's Crush; Mitelman & Von Kohorn, 2012) and adults with disabilities (for example, Friendships and Dating; see Ward et al., 2013; Ward et al., 2012) are particularly promising.

The rights of people with disabilities to bear children, cohabitate, and marry are not fully embraced by current laws and policies (see, for example, the *Buck v. Bell* 1927 Supreme Court decision); the interviewed social workers support self-determination while also carefully balancing clients' needs (for example, aiming to keep their federal and state benefits). They educate their clients about their choices and consequences of their choices (for example, potential marriage among two people with disabilities living in group homes and group home cohabitation policies). Social workers ensure that people with disabilities who have children obtain the resources necessary to raise children, such as housing, health care, finances, and food.

Social workers normalize intimate and sexual needs of people with disabilities by educating family members and other professionals. This is necessary to create full sexual citizenship of people with disabilities throughout the life course. We should note that some social workers whom we contacted to be interviewed did not embrace the importance of the intimate and sexual needs of their clients. One such social worker reported that discussing the topic of sexuality with her clients was unethical. This may have been true because of institutional policies, such as abstinence-only curricula in schools. We hope that this book has opened your eyes to the need to normalize intimacy and the sexual needs of people with disabilities and that you will fully include people with disabilities in your intimate and sexual health practice as a social worker. If you work for an institution that disables your clients' ability to engage in intimate and sexual relationships equal to others, we hope that you will advocate for changes to those policies.

References

Adams, H. L., & Williams, L. R. (2011a). Advice from teens to teens about dating: Implications for healthy relationships. *Children and Youth Services Review, 33,* 254–264.

Adams, H. L., & Williams, L. R. (2011b). What they wish they would have known: Support for comprehensive sexual education from Mexican American and white adolescents' dating and sexual desires. *Children and Youth Services Review, 33,* 1875–1885.

Ajzen, I. (1991). The theory of planned behavior. *Organizational Behavior and Human Decision Processes, 50,* 179–211.

Alleyne-Green, B., Coleman-Cowger, V. H., & Henry, D. B. (2012). Dating violence perpetration and/or victimization and associated sexual risk behaviors among a sample of inner-city African American and Hispanic adolescent females. *Journal of Interpersonal Violence, 27,* 1457–1473.

Alriksson-Schmidt, A. I., Armour, B. S., & Thibadeau, J. K. (2010). Are adolescent girls with a physical disability at increased risk for sexual violence? *Journal of Social Health, 80,* 361–367.

American Psychiatric Association. (2000). *Diagnostic and statistical manual of mental disorders* (4th ed., text rev.). Washington, DC: Author.

American Psychiatric Association. (2013). *Diagnostic and statistical manual of mental disorders* (5th ed.). Arlington, VA: American Psychiatric Publishing.

Americans with Disabilities Act of 1990, P.L. 101-336, 104 Stat. 328 (1990).

Anastasiou, D., & Kauffman, J. M. (2013). The social model of disability: Dichotomy between impairment and disability. *Journal of Medicine and Philosophy, 38*, 441–459.

Ashford, J. B., & LeCroy, C. W. (2013). *Human behavior in the social environment: A multidimensional perspective* (5th ed.). Belmont, CA: Brooks/Cole.

Associated Press. (2013, May 7). Lawsuit challenges rule that bars mentally disabled married couples from sharing group home bedroom. *New York Daily News.* Retrieved from http://www.nydailynews.com/new-york/disabled-newlyweds-forced-live-article-1.1337788

Azzopardi-Lane, C., & Callus, A. M. (2015). Constructing sexual identities: People with intellectual disability talking about sexuality. *British Journal of Learning Disabilities, 43*(1), 32–37.

Baladerian, N. J., Coleman, T. R., & Stream, J. (2013). *Abuse of people with disabilities victims and their families speak out: A report on the 2012 National Survey on Abuse of People with Disabilities.* Los Angeles: Spectrum Institute. Retrieved from http://disability-abuse.com/survey/survey-report.pdf

Ballan, M. S. (2008). Disability and sexuality within social work education in the USA and Canada: The social model of disability as a lens for practice. *Social Work Education, 27*, 194–202.

Ballan, M. S. (2012). Parental perspectives of communication about sexuality in families of children with autism spectrum disorders. *Journal of Autism and Developmental Disorders, 42*, 676–684.

Barnard-Brak, L., Schmidt, M., Chesnut, S., Wei, T., & Richman, D. (2014). Predictors of access to sex education for children with intellectual disabilities in public schools. *Mental Retardation, 52*, 85–97.

Bartlett, P. (2010). Sex, dementia, capacity and care homes. *Liverpool Law Review, 31*, 137–154.

Bates, C., Terry, L., & Popple, K. (2016). Partner selection for people with intellectual disabilities. *Journal of Applied Research in Intellectual Disabilities.* doi:10.1111/jar.12254

Bauer, M., Fetherstonhaugh, D., Tarzia, L., Nay, R., & Beattie, E. (2014). Supporting residents' expression of sexuality: The initial construction of a sexuality assessment tool for residential aged care facilities. *BMC Geriatrics, 14*(1), 82–87.

Bean, K. F., & Krcek, T. (2012). The integration of disability content into social work education: An examination of infused and dedicated models. *Advances in Social Work, 13*, 633–647.

Belluck, P. (2015, April 13). Sex, dementia and a husband on trial at age 78. *New York Times*. Retrieved from http://www.nytimes.com/2015/04/14/health/sex-dementia-and-a-husband-henry-rayhons-on-trial-at-age-78.html?_r=0

Bermea, A. M., Rueda, H. A., & Toews, M. L. (in press). Queerness and dating violence among adolescent mothers in foster care. *Affilia*.

Beyers, W., & Seiffge-Krenke, I. (2010). Does identity precede intimacy? Testing Erikson's theory on romantic development in emerging adults of the 21st century. *Journal of Adolescent Research, 25*, 387–415.

Blatt, S. J., & Blass, R. B. (1996). Relatedness and self-definition: A dialectic model of personality development. In G. Noam & K. Fischer (Eds.), *Development and vulnerability in close relationships* (pp. 309–338). Hillsdale, NJ: Erlbaum.

Blum, R. W., Resnick, M. D., Nelson, R., & St. Germaine, A. (1991). Family and peer issues among adolescents with spina bifida and cerebral palsy. *Pediatrics, 88*, 280–285.

Bremness, A., & Polzin, W. (2014). Commentary: Developmental trauma disorder: A missed opportunity in DSM V. *Journal of the Canadian Academy of Child and Adolescent Psychiatry, 23*, 142–145.

Bronfenbrenner, U. (1977). Toward an experimental ecology of human development. *American Psychologist, 32*, 513–531.

Bronfenbrenner, U. (1979). *The ecology of human development*. Cambridge, MA: Harvard University Press.

Brownridge, D. A. (2006). Partner violence against women with disabilities: Prevalence, risk, and explanations. *Violence against Women, 12*, 805–822.

Buck v. Bell, 274, U.S. Supreme Court 200 (1927).

Burgdorf, R. (1980). *The legal rights of handicapped persons*. Baltimore: Paul H. Brookes.

Burt, R. A. (1973). Legal restrictions on sexual and familial relations of mental retardates: Old laws, new guises. In F. F. de la Cruz & G. D. La Veck (Eds.), *Human sexuality and the mentally retarded* (pp. 206–214). New York: Bruner/Mazel.

Carver, K., Joyner, K., & Udry, J. R. (2003). National estimates of adolescent romantic relationships. In P. Flörsheim (Ed.), *Adolescent romantic relations and sexual behavior: Theory, research, and practical implications* (pp. 23–56). Mahwah, NJ: Erlbaum.

Centers for Disease Control and Prevention. (2000). Surveillance for characteristics of health education among secondary schools: School health education programs, 1998. *Morbidity and Mortality Weekly Report, 49*(SS08), 1–41.

Centers for Disease Control and Prevention. (2015). *Child development: Positive parenting tips.* Retrieved from http://www.cdc.gov/ncbddd/childdevelopment/positiveparenting/index.html

Christensen, M. C., Wright, R., & Dunn, J. (2016). "It's awkward stuff": Conversations about sexuality with young children. *Child & Family Social Work.* doi:10.1111/cfs.12287

Cimino, A. N. (in press). Sex work and adult prostitution: From entry to exit. In M. Bourke & V. Van Hasselt (Eds.), *Handbook of behavioral criminology: Contemporary strategies and issues.* New York: Springer.

Collins, W. A. (2003). More than myth: The developmental significance of romantic relationships during adolescence. *Journal of Research on Adolescence, 13*(1), 1–24.

Connolly, J. A., & Johnson, A. M. (1996). Adolescents' romantic relationships and the structure and quality of their close interpersonal ties. *Personal Relationships, 3*, 185–195.

Connolly, J. A., & McIsaac, C. (2009a). Adolescents' explanations for romantic dissolutions: A developmental perspective. *Journal of Adolescence, 32,* 1209–1223.

Connolly, J. A., & McIsaac, C. (2009b). Romantic relationships in adolescence. In R. Lerner & L. Steinberg (Eds.), *Handbook of adolescent psychology* (3rd ed., pp. 104–151). Hoboken, NJ: Wiley.

Connolly, J. A., & McIsaac, C. (2011). Romantic relationships in adolescence. In M. K. Underwood & L. H. Rosen (Eds.), *Social development: Relationships in infancy, childhood, and adolescence* (pp. 180–200). New York: Guilford Press.

Constantine, N. A., Jerman, P., & Huang, A. X. (2007). California parents' preferences and beliefs regarding school-based sex education policy. *Perspectives on Sexual and Reproductive Health, 39*, 167–175.

Council on Social Work Education. (2001). *Educational practices and accreditation standards.* Retrieved from http://www.cswe.org/file.aspx?id=14115

Council on Social Work Education. (2008). *Educational practices and accreditation standards.* Retrieved from http://www.cswe.org/Accreditation/Handbook.aspx

Crossland, C., Palmer, J., & Brooks, A. (2013). NIJ's program of research on violence against American Indian and Alaska native women. *Violence against Women, 19,* 771–790.

Cunningham, P. W. (2017, May 4). Planned Parenthood defunded for one year under GOP health bill. *Washington Post.* Retrieved from https://www

.washingtonpost.com/news/powerpost/wp/2017/05/04/planned-parenthood-defunded-for-one-year-under-gop-health-bill/?utm_term=.d08217c03617

De Boer, A., Pijl, S. J., Post, W., & Minnaert, A. (2013). Peer acceptance and friendships of students with disabilities in general education: The role of child, peer, and classroom variables. *Social Development, 22,* 831–844.

De Laat, S., Freriksen, E., & Vervloed, M.P.J. (2013). Attitudes of children and adolescents toward persons who are deaf, blind, paralyzed or intellectually disabled. *Research in Developmental Disabilities, 34,* 855–863.

Dibble Institute. (n.d.). *Mike's crush.* Retrieved from http://www.dibbleinstitute.org/mikes-crush/

Di Napoli, E. A., Breland, G. L., & Allen, R. S. (2013). Staff knowledge and perceptions of sexuality and dementia of older adults in nursing homes. *Journal of Aging and Health, 25,* 1087–1105.

Dolak, K. (2013). Mentally disabled couple's legal battle ends with a new home. *ABC News.* Retrieved from http://abcnews.go.com/US/mentally-disabled-couples-legal-battle-ends-home/story?id=19237103

Donenberg, G. R., Emerson, E., Brown, L. K., Houck, C., & Mackesy-Amiti, M. E. (2012). Sexual experience among emotionally and behaviorally disordered students in therapeutic day schools: An ecological examination of adolescent risk. *Journal of Pediatric Psychology, 37,* 904–913.

Dourado, M., Finamore, C., Barroso, M. F., Santos, R., & Laks, J. (2010). Sexual satisfaction in dementia: Perspectives of patients and spouses. *Sexuality and Disability, 28,* 195–203.

Doyle, J. (2008). Improving sexual health information for young people with learning disabilities. *Pediatric Care, 20*(4), 26–28.

Dunkle, K. L., Wingood, G. M., Camp, C. M., & DiClemente, R. J. (2010). Economically motivated relationships and transactional sex among unmarried African American and white women: Results from a U.S. national telephone survey. *Public Health Reports, 125,* 90–100.

East, L. J., & Orchard, T. R. (2014). Somebody else's job: Experiences of sex education among health professionals, parents and adolescents with physical disabilities in southwestern Ontario. *Sexuality and Disability, 32,* 335–350.

Eaton, D. K., Lowry, R., Brener, N. D., Kann, L., Romero, L., & Wechsler, H. (2011). Trends in human immunodeficiency virus- and sexually transmitted disease-related risk behaviors among U.S. high school students, 1991–2009. *American Journal of Preventive Medicine, 40,* 427–433.

Education for All Handicapped Children Act, P.L. 94-142, 89 Stat. 773 (1975) (codified as amended at 20 U.S.C. § 1400-61 [1982]).

Elliott, D. E., Bjelajac, P., Fallot, R. D., Markoff, L. S., & Reed, B. G. (2005). Trauma-informed or trauma-denied: Principles and implementation of trauma-informed services for women. *Journal of Community Psychology, 33*, 461–477.

Evans, D. S., McGuire, B. E., Healy, E., & Carley, S. N. (2009). Sexuality and personal relationships for people with an intellectual disability. Part II: Staff and family carer perspectives. *Journal of Intellectual Disability Research, 53*, 913–921.

Every Student Succeeds Act, S. 1177, 114th Cong. (2015). Retrieved from https://www.congress.gov/bill/114th-congress/senate-bill/1177/text#toc-H5C8F28DD26484C0DBC5342F25E6823AC

Fader Wilkenfeld, B., & Ballan, M. S. (2011). Educators' attitudes and beliefs towards the sexuality of individuals with developmental disabilities. *Sexuality and Disability, 29*, 351–361.

Family and Youth Services Bureau. (2015a). *State abstinence education grant program fact sheet.* Retrieved from http://www.acf.hhs.gov/programs/fysb/resource/aegp-fact-sheet

Family and Youth Services Bureau. (2015b). *State personal responsibility education program fact sheet.* Retrieved from http://www.acf.hhs.gov/programs/fysb/resource/prep-fact-sheet

Fattore, T., Mason, J., & Watson, E. (2009). When children are asked about their wellbeing: Towards a framework for guiding policy. *Child Indicators Research, 2*, 57–77.

Fiduccia, B. W. (2000). Current issues in sexuality and the disability movement. *Sexuality and Disability, 18*, 167–174.

Fine, M. (1988). Sexuality, schooling, and adolescent females: The missing discourse of desire. *Harvard Educational Review, 58*(1), 29–53.

Fitzgerald, C., & Withers, P. (2013). "I don't know what a proper woman means": What women with intellectual disabilities think about sex, sexuality and themselves. *British Journal of Learning Disabilities, 41*(1), 5–12.

Foley, K. R., Blackmore, A. M., Girdler, S., O'Donnell, M., Glauert, R., Llewellyn, G., & Leonard, H. (2012). To feel belonged: The voices of children and youth with disabilities on the meaning of wellbeing. *Child Indicators Research, 5*, 375–391.

Galea, J., Butler, J., Iacono, T., & Leighton, D. (2004). The assessment of sexual knowledge in people with intellectual disability. *Journal of Intellectual and Developmental Disability, 29,* 350–365.

Gonzalez-Guarda, R. M., Vermeesch, A. L., Florom-Smith, A. L., McCabe, B. E., & Peragallo, N. P. (2013). Birthplace, culture, self-esteem, and intimate partner violence among community-dwelling Hispanic women. *Violence against Women, 19,* 6–23.

Greydanus, D. E., & Omar, H. A. (2008). Sexuality issues and gynecologic care of adolescents with developmental disabilities. *Developmental Disabilities, 55,* 1315–1335.

Grover, S. R. (2011). Gynaecological issues in adolescents with disability. *Journal of Paediatrics and Child Health, 47,* 610–613.

Hahn, J. W., McCormick, M. C., Silverman, J. G., Robinson, E. B., & Koenen, K. C. (2014). Examining the impact of disability status on intimate partner violence victimization in a population sample. *Journal of Interpersonal Violence, 29,* 3063–3085.

Haider, S., Stoffel, C., Donenberg, G., & Geller, S. (2013). Reproductive health disparities: A focus on family planning and prevention among minority women and adolescents. *Global Advances in Health and Medicine, 2*(5), 94–99.

Hall, J. E., & Sawyer, H. W. (1978). Sexual policies for the mentally retarded. *Sexuality and Disability, 1,* 34–43.

Harden, K. P. (2014). A sex-positive framework for research on adolescent sexuality. *Perspectives on Psychological Science, 9,* 455–469.

Hartling, L., Milne, A., Tjosvold, L., Wrightson, D., Gallivan, J., & Newton, A. S. (2014). A systematic review of interventions to support siblings of children with chronic illness or disability. *Journal of Paediatrics and Child Health, 50*(10), E26–E38.

Healy, E., McGuire, B. E., Evans, D. S., & Carley, S. N. (2009). Sexuality and personal relationships for people with an intellectual disability: Part I: Service-user perspectives. *Journal of Intellectual Disability Research, 53,* 905–912.

Hershkowitz, I., Lamb, M. E., & Horowitz, D. (2007). Victimization of children with disabilities. *American Journal of Orthopsychiatry, 77,* 629–635.

Hillman, J. (2008). Sexual issues and aging within the context of work with older adult patients. *Professional Psychology: Research and Practice, 39,* 290–297.

Höglund, B., Lindgren, P., & Larsson, M. (2012). Pregnancy and birth outcomes of women with intellectual disability in Sweden: A National Register study. *Acta obstetricia et gynecologica Scandinavica, 91,* 1381–1387.

Hossfeld, B. (2007). Developing friendships and peer relationships: Building social support with the Girls Circle program. In C. W. LeCroy & J. E. Mann (Eds.), *Handbook of prevention and intervention programs for adolescent girls* (pp. 41–80). Hoboken, NJ: Wiley.

Hwang, K., Johnston, M., & Smith, J. K. (2007). Romantic attachment in individuals with physical disabilities. *Rehabilitation Psychology, 52,* 184–195.

Hyde, J. S., & DeLamater, J. D. (2008). *Understanding human sexuality* (10th ed.). Boston: McGraw-Hill Higher Education.

Individuals with Disabilities Education Act, 20 U.S.C. § 1400 (2004).

Janus, A. L. (2009). Disability and the transition to adulthood. *Social Forces, 88*(1), 99–120.

Jeffries, W. L., IV, Dodge, B., Bandiera, F. C., & Reece, M. (2010). Beyond abstinence-only: Relationships between abstinence education and comprehensive topic instruction. *Sex Education, 10,* 171–185.

Jones, L., Bellis, M. A., Wood, S., Hughes, K., McCoy, E., Eckley, L., et al. (2012). Prevalence and risk of violence against children with disabilities: A systematic review and meta-analysis of observational studies. *Lancet, 380,* 899–907.

Kann, L., Brener, N., McManus, T., & Wechsler, H. (2012). HIV, other STD, and pregnancy prevention education in public secondary schools—45 states, 2008–2010. *Morbidity and Mortality Weekly Report, 61,* 222–228.

Kellogg, N. D. (2010). Sexual behaviors in children: Evaluation and management. *American Family Physician, 82,* 1233–1238.

Kempton, W., & Kahn, E. (1991). Sexuality and people with intellectual disabilities: A historical perspective. *Sexuality and Disability, 9,* 93–110.

Kerr, S. (2000). The application of the Americans with Disabilities Act to the termination of parental rights of individuals with mental disabilities. *Journal of Contemporary Health, Law, and Policy, 16,* 387–426.

Kim, E. (2011). Asexuality in disability narratives. *Sexualities, 14,* 479–493.

Larkin, H., Felitti, V. J., & Anda, R. F. (2014). Social work and adverse childhood experiences research: Implications for practice and health policy. *Social Work in Public Health, 29*(1), 1–16.

Larson, R. W., Clore, G. L., & Wood, G. A. (1999). The emotions of romantic relationships: Do they wreak havoc on adolescents. In W. Furman, B. Bradford Brown, & C. Feiring (Eds.), *Development of romantic relationships in adolescence* (pp. 19–49). Cambridge, UK: Cambridge University Press.

Laws, J., Parish, S., Scheyett, A., & Egan, C. (2010). Preparation of social workers to support people with developmental disabilities. *Journal of Teaching in Social Work, 30*, 317–333.

Leyson, J. F. J. (Ed.). (2013). *Sexual rehabilitation of the spinal-cord-injured patient.* Clifton, NJ: Humana Press.

Lindsay, W., Steptoe, L., & Haut, F. (2012). Brief report: The sexual and physical abuse histories of offenders with intellectual disability. *Journal of Intellectual Disability Research, 56*, 326–331.

Linton, K. F. (2015). Interpersonal violence and traumatic brain injuries among Native Americans. *Brain Injury, 29*, 639–643.

Liu, C. (2017). Is she smart? *TEDx Camarillo* [Video file]. Retrieved from https://www.youtube.com/watch?v=mr_Fff6ZiXI

Llewellyn, G., & Hindmarsh, G. (2015). Parents with intellectual disability in a population context. *Current Developmental Disorders Reports, 2*, 119–126.

Löfgren-Mårtenson, L. (2011). "I want to do it right!": A pilot study of Swedish sex education and young people with intellectual disabilities. *Sexuality and Disability, 30*, 209–225.

Löfgren-Mårtenson, L. (2013). "Hip to be crip?" About crip theory, sexuality and people with intellectual disabilities. *Sexuality and Disability, 31*, 413–424.

Mandell, D. S., Eleey, C. C., Cederbaum, J. A., Noll, E., Hutchinson, K., Jemmott, L. S., & Blank, M. B. (2008). Sexually transmitted infection among adolescents receiving special education services. *Journal of School Health, 78*, 382–388.

Martinez, G., Copen, C. E., & Abma, J. C. (2011). Teenagers in the United States: Sexual activity, contraceptive use, and childbearing, 2006–2010 National Survey of Family Growth. *Vital and Health Statistics, 31*, 1–35.

McBride Murry, V., Berkel, C., Gaylord-Harden, N. K., Copeland-Linder, N., & Nation, M. (2011). Neighborhood poverty and adolescent development. *Journal of Research on Adolescence, 21*, 114–128.

McCarthy, M. (2009). Contraception and women with intellectual disabilities. *Journal of Applied Research in Intellectual Disabilities, 22*, 363–369.

McKenzie, J. A., & Swartz, L. (2011). The shaping of sexuality in children with disabilities: AQ methodological study. *Sexuality and Disability, 29*, 363–376.

McLay, L., Carnett, A., Tyler-Merrick, G., & van der Meer, L. (2015). A systematic review of interventions for inappropriate sexual behavior of children and adolescents with developmental disabilities. *Review Journal of Autism and Developmental Disorders, 2*, 357–373.

McRuer, R. (2006). *Crip theory: Cultural signs of queerness and disability.* New York: New York University Press.

Milbrath, C., Ohlson, B., & Eyre, S. L. (2009). Analyzing cultural models in adolescent accounts of romantic relationships. *Journal of Research on Adolescence, 19,* 313–351.

Mitelman, S., & Von Kohorn, O. (2012). Social signals—Mike's crush. *American Journal of Sexuality Education, 7,* 282–284.

Montgomery, M. J. (2005). Psychosocial intimacy and identity: From early adolescence to emerging adulthood. *Journal of Adolescent Research, 20,* 346–374.

Morin, A. J., Maïano, C., Marsh, H. W., Janosz, M., & Nagengast, B. (2011). The longitudinal interplay of adolescents' self-esteem and body image: A conditional autoregressive latent trajectory analysis. *Multivariate Behavioral Research, 46,* 157–201.

Mulhern, T. J. (1975). Survey of reported sexual behavior and policies characterizing residential facilities for retarded citizens. *American Journal of Mental Deficiency, 79,* 670–673.

Murphy, N. A., Elias, E. R., & Council on Children with Disabilities. (2006). Sexuality of children and adolescents with developmental disabilities. *Pediatrics, 118,* 398–403.

National Association of Social Workers. (1979). *Code of ethics of the National Association of Social Workers.* Retrieved from https://www.socialworkers.org/nasw/ethics/ethicshistory.asp

National Association of Social Workers. (2001). *Code of ethics of the National Association of Social Workers.* Retrieved from https://www.socialworkers.org/nasw/ethics/ethicshistory.asp

National Association of Social Workers. (2006). *Assuring the sufficiency of a frontline workforce: A national study of licensed social workers.* Retrieved from http://workforce.socialworkers.org/studies/nasw_06_execsummary.pdf

National Association of Social Workers. (2015a). *Code of ethics of the National Association of Social Workers.* Retrieved from http://www.naswdc.org/pubs/code/code.asp

National Association of Social Workers. (2015b). *Standards and indicators for cultural competence in social work practice.* Retrieved from http://www.socialworkers.org/practice/standards/PRA-BRO-253150-CC-Standards.pdf

National Institutes of Health. (2013). *Disability in older adults* [NIH Fact Sheet]. Retrieved from https://report.nih.gov/nihfactsheets/ViewFactSheet.aspx?csid=37

Neuhaus, R., Smith, C., & Burgdorf, M. (2014). Equality for people with disabilities, then and now. *GPSolo, 31*(6), 46–51.

Newall, N. E., Chipperfield, J. G., Bailis, D. S., & Stewart, T. L. (2013). Consequences of loneliness on physical activity and mortality in older adults and the power of positive emotions. *Health Psychology, 32,* 921–924.

Nguyen, T. T. A., Liamputtong, P., & Monfries, M. (2016). Reproductive and sexual health of people with physical disabilities: A metasynthesis. *Sexuality and Disability, 34,* 3–26.

Nichols, S., & Blakeley-Smith, A. (2010). "I'm not sure we're ready for this . . .": Working with families toward facilitating healthy sexuality for individuals with autism spectrum disorders. *Social Work in Mental Health, 8,* 72–91.

Oliver, M. (1990). *The politics of disablement.* Basingstoke, UK: Macmillan.

Oliver, M. (1996). *Understanding disability: From theory to practice.* Basingstoke, UK: Macmillan.

One Circle Foundation. (2012). *The Council for Boys and Young Men.* Retrieved from https://onecirclefoundation.org/material-tc.aspx

Organista, K. C. (2007). The Latino family. In K.C. Organista (Ed.), *Solving Latino psychosocial and health problems: Theory, practice, and populations.* (pp. 141–180). Hoboken, NJ: Wiley.

Ortman, J. M., Velkoff, V. A., & Hogan, H. (2014). *An aging nation: The older population in the United States. Population estimates and projections.* Retrieved from https://www.census.gov/prod/2014pubs/p25-1140.pdf

O'Toole, C. J., & Doe, T. (2002). Sexuality and disabled parents with disabled children. *Sexuality and Disability, 20,* 89–101.

Padgett, D. K. (2008). *Qualitative methods in social work research.* Thousand Oaks, CA: Sage Publications.

Panesar, S., & Wolbring, G. (2014). Analysis of North American newspaper coverage of bionics using the disability studies framework. *Technologies, 2*(1), 1–30.

Parchomiuk, M. (2012). Specialists and sexuality of individuals with disability. *Sexuality and Disability, 30,* 407–419.

Patient Protection and Affordable Care Act, 42 U.S.C. § 18001 (2010).

Peers, D., Spencer-Cavaliere, N., & Eales, L. (2014). Say what you mean: Rethinking disability language. *Adapted Physical Activity Quarterly, 31,* 265–282.

Perissinotto, C. M., Cenzer, I. S., & Covinsky, K. E. (2012). Loneliness in older persons: A predictor of functional decline and death. *Archives of Internal Medicine, 172,* 1078–1084.

Pfeiffer, D. (1994). Eugenics and disability discrimination. *Disability & Society,* *9,* 481–499.

Planned Parenthood. (2017). *2015–2016 annual report.* Retrieved from https://www.plannedparenthood.org/uploads/filer_public/18/40/1840b04b-55d3-4c00-959d-11817023ffc8/20170526_annualreport_p02_singles.pdf

Pownall, J. D., Jahoda, A., & Hastings, R. P. (2012). Sexuality and sex education of adolescents with intellectual disability: Mothers' attitudes, experiences, and support needs. *Intellectual and Developmental Disabilities, 50,* 140–154.

Purvis, K. B., Cross, D. R., & Pennings, J. S. (2009). Trust-based relational intervention: Interactive principles for adopted children with special social emotional needs. *Journal of Humanistic Counseling, Education and Development, 48*(1), 3–22.

Quinn, P. (1995). Social work education and disability: Benefiting from the impact of the ADA. *Journal of Teaching in Social Work, 12*(1), 55–71.

Rains, R. E. (2005). Disability and family relationship: Marriage penalties and support anomalies. *Georgia State Law Review, 22,* 561–596.

Rand, S. (2015). Real marriage penalty: How welfare law discourages marriage despite public policy statements to the contrary—and what can be done about it. *University of the District of Columbia Law Review, 18*(1), 93–144.

Rauf, B., Saleem, N., Clawson, R., Sanghera, M., & Marston, G. (2013). Forced marriage: Implications for mental health and intellectual disability services. *Advances in Psychiatric Treatment, 19,* 135–143.

Ray, F., Marks, C., & Bray-Garretson, H. (2004). Challenges to treating adolescents with Asperger's syndrome who are sexually abusive. *Sexual Addiction & Compulsivity, 11,* 265–285.

Rehabilitation Act, P. L. 93-112, Title V, Section 504 (1973).

Rohleder, P. (2010). Educators' ambivalence and managing anxiety in providing sex education for people with learning disabilities. *Psychodynamic Practice, 16,* 165–182.

Rueda, H. A., Bolin, S., Linton, K. F., Williams, L. R., & Pesta, E. (2016). Social workers' roles in supporting the sexual and relational health of children with disabilities. *Child & Adolescent Social Work Journal.* Advance online publication. doi:10.1007/s10560-016-0469-x

Rueda, H. A., Nagoshi, J. L., & Williams, L. R. (2014). Mexican American and European American adolescents' dating experiences across the ecosystem: Implications for healthy relationships within an ecodevelopmental framework. *Journal of Human Behavior in the Social Environment, 24,* 358–376.

Rutman, S., Taualii, M., Ned, D., & Tetrick, C. (2012). Reproductive health and sexual violence among urban American Indian and Alaska native young women: Select findings from the National Survey of Family Growth (2002). *Maternal and Child Health Journal, 16*(2), S347–S352.

Sabina, C., Cuevas, C. A., & Schally, J. L. (2012). The cultural influences on help-seeking among a national sample of victimized Latino women. *American Journal of Community Psychology, 49*, 347–363.

Schick, V., Herbenick, D., Reece, M., Sanders, S. A., Dodge, B., Middlestadt, S. E., & Fortenberry, J. D. (2010). Sexual behaviors, condom use, and sexual health of Americans over 50: Implications for sexual health promotion for older adults. *Journal of Sexual Medicine, 7*(Suppl. 5), 315–329.

Servais, L. (2006). Sexual health care in persons with intellectual disability. *Mental Retardation and Developmental Disabilities, 12*(1), 48–56.

Shakespeare, T. (2000). Disabled sexuality: Toward rights and recognition. *Sexuality and Disability, 18*, 159–166.

Shandra, C. L. (2011). Life-course transitions among adolescents with and without disabilities. *International Journal of Sociology, 41*(1), 67–86.

Shandra, C. L., & Chowdhury, A. R. (2012). The first sexual experience among adolescent girls with and without disabilities. *Journal of Youth and Adolescence, 41*, 515–532.

Shildrick, M. (2013). Sexual citizenship, governance and disability: From Foucault to Deleuze. In S. Roseneil (Ed.), *Beyond citizenship? Feminism and the transformation of belonging* (pp. 138–159). London: Palgrave Macmillan.

Siebelink, E. M., de Jong, M.D.T., Taal, E., & Roelvink, L. (2006). Sexuality and people with intellectual disabilities: Assessment of knowledge, experiences, and needs. *Mental Retardation, 44*, 283–294.

SIECUS. (2009, October). *Fact sheet: What the research says . . . comprehensive sex education.* Retrieved from http://www.siecus.org/index.cfm?fuseaction=Page.ViewPage&PageID=1193

Singleton, P. (2012). Insult to injury disability, earnings, and divorce. *Journal of Human Resources, 47*, 972–990.

Social Security. (2016). *SSI federal payment amounts.* Retrieved from https://www.ssa.gov/oact/cola/SSIamts.html

Stanger-Hall, K. F., & Hall, D. W. (2011). Abstinence-only education and teen pregnancy rates: Why we need comprehensive sex education in the U.S. *PLOS ONE, 6*(10), e24658.

Steese, S., Dollette, M., Phillips, W., & Hossfeld, E. (2006). Understanding Girls' Circle as an intervention on perceived social support, body image, self-efficacy, locus of control, and self-esteem. *Adolescence, 41*(161), 55–74.

Sternberg, R. J. (1986). A triangular theory of love. *Psychological Review, 93*, 119–135.

Stokes, M. A., & Kaur, A. (2005). High-functioning autism and sexuality: A a parental perspective. *Autism, 9*, 266–289.

Swango-Wilson, A. (2009). Perception of sex education for individuals with developmental and cognitive disability: A four cohort study. *Sexuality and Disability, 27*, 223–228.

Swango-Wilson, A. (2010). Systems theory and the development of sexual identity for individuals with intellectual/developmental disability. *Sexuality and Disability, 28*, 157–164.

Swango-Wilson, A. (2011). Meaningful sex education programs for individuals with intellectual/developmental disabilities. *Sexuality and Disability, 29*, 113–118.

Tang, S. L. (2014). When yes might mean no: Standardizing state criteria to evaluate the capacity to consent to sexual activity for elderly with neurocognitive disorders. *Elder Law Journal, 22*, 449–490.

Taylor Gomez, M. (2012). The s words: Sexuality, sensuality, sexual expression and people with intellectual disability. *Sexuality and Disability, 30*, 237–245.

Tepper, M. S. (2000). Sexuality and disability: The missing discourse of pleasure. *Sexuality and disability, 18*, 283–290.

Tilley, E., Walmsley, J., Earle, S., & Atkinson, D. (2012). "The silence is roaring": Sterilization, reproductive rights and women with intellectual disabilities. *Disability & Society, 27*, 413–426.

Tissot, C. (2009). Establishing a sexual identity: Case studies of learners with autism and learning difficulties. *Autism: The International Journal of Research and Practice, 13*, 511–566.

Tobin, M. (2011). Put me first: The importance of person-first language. *Innovations*. Retrieved from http://www.ttacnews.vcu.edu/2011/05/put-me-first-the-importance-of-person-first-language/

Tumin, D. (2016). Marriage trends among Americans with childhood-onset disabilities, 1997–2013. *Disability and Health Journal, 9*, 713–718.

Turner, H. A., Vanderminden, J., Finklehor, D., Hamby, S., & Shattuck, A. (2011). Disability and victimization in a national sample of children and youth. *Child Maltreatment, 16*, 275–286.

UAA Center for Human Development. (2017). *Friendships and dating.* Retrieved from https://www.uaa.alaska.edu/academics/college-of-health/departments/center-for-human-development/friendships-and-dating/index.cshtml

Updegraff, K. A., Umaña-Taylor, A., McHale, S. M., Wheeler, L. A., & Perez-Brena, N. J. (2012). Mexican-origin youth's cultural orientations and adjustment: Changes from early to late adolescence. *Child Development, 83,* 1655–1671.

U.S. Department of Health and Human Services. (2016). *Updated findings from the HHS teen pregnancy prevention evidence review: July 2014 through August 2015.* Retrieved from http://tppevidencereview.aspe.hhs.gov/pdfs/Summary_of_findings_2015.pdf

Vasilenko, S. A., Kreager, D. A., & Lefkowitz, E. S. (2015). Gender, contraceptive attitudes, and condom use in adolescent romantic relationships: A dyadic approach. *Journal of Research on Adolescence, 25*(1), 51–62.

Wade, H. A. (2002). Discrimination, sexuality, and people with significant disabilities: Issues of access and the right to sexual expression in the United States. *Disability Studies Quarterly, 22*(4), 9–27.

Wallace, M., & Safer, M. (2009). Hypersexuality among cognitively impaired older adults. *Geriatric Nursing, 30,* 230–237.

Ward, K. M., Atkinson, J. P., Smith, C. A., & Windsor, R. (2013). A friendships and dating program for adults with intellectual and developmental disabilities: A formative evaluation. *Intellectual and Developmental Disabilities, 51,* 22–32.

Ward, K. M., Bosek, R. L., & Trimble, E. L. (2010). Romantic relationships and interpersonal violence among adults with developmental disabilities. *Intellectual and Developmental Disabilities, 48,* 89–98.

Ward, K. M., Windsor, R., & Atkinson, J. P. (2012). A process evaluation of the Friendships and Dating Program for adults with developmental disabilities: Measuring the fidelity of program delivery. *Research in Developmental Disabilities, 33*(1), 69–75.

Watson, S. L., Richards, D. A., Miodrag, N., & Fedoroff, J. P. (2012). Sex and genes, part 1: Sexuality and Down, Prader-Willi, and Williams syndromes. *Intellectual and Developmental Disabilities, 50,* 155–168.

Weeks, J. (1998). The sexual citizen. *Theory, Culture, and Society, 15*(3), 35–52.

Wells, T., Sandefur, G. D., & Hogan, D. P. (2003). What happens after the high school years among young persons with disabilities. *Social Forces, 82,* 803–832.

Wiegerink, D.J.H.D., Roebroeck, M. E., Donkervoort, M., Stam, H. J., & Cohen-Kettenis, P. T. (2006). Social and sexual relationships of adolescents and young adults with cerebral palsy: A review. *Clinical Rehabilitation, 20,* 1023–1031.

Wild, T. A., Kelly, S. M., Blackburn, M. V., & Ryan, C. L. (2014). Adults with visual impairments report on their sex education experiences. *Journal of Blindness Innovation & Research, 4*(2), 1–1.

Williams, L. R. (2014). Experiences with violence in Mexican American and European American high school dating relationships. *Children & Schools, 36*, 115–124.

Williams, L. R., & Adams, H. L. (2013a). Friends with benefits or "friends" with deficits? The meaning and contexts of uncommitted sexual relationships among Mexican American and European American adolescents. *Children and Youth Services Review, 35*, 1110–1117.

Williams, L. R., & Adams, H. L. (2013b). Parties, drugs, and high school hook-ups: Socio-emotional challenges for European and Mexican American adolescents. *Affilia, 28*, 240–255.

Williams, L. R., & Hickle, K. E. (2010). "I know what love means": Qualitative descriptions from Mexican American and white adolescents. *Journal of Human Behavior in the Social Environment, 20*, 581–600.

Williams, L. R., & Hickle, K. (2011). "He cheated on me, I cheated on him back": Mexican American and white adolescents' perceptions of cheating in romantic relationships. *Journal of Adolescence, 34*, 1005–1016.

Winges-Yanez, N. (2014). Discourse analysis of curriculum on sexuality education: FLASH for special education. *Sexuality and Disability, 32*, 485–498.

Wolowicz-Ruszkowska, A. (2015). How Polish women with disabilities challenge the meaning of motherhood. *Psychology of Women Quarterly, 40*(1), 1–16.

Woodley, M. A. (2009). Inbreeding depression and IQ in a study of 72 countries. *Intelligence, 37*, 268–276.

World Health Organization. (2017). *International classification of functioning, disability, and health.* Retrieved from http://www.who.int/classifications/icf/en/

Wright, E. R., McCabe, H., & Kooreman, H. E. (2012). Institutional capacity to respond to the ethical challenges of patient sexual expression in state psychiatric hospitals in the United States. *Journal of Ethics in Mental Health, 7*, 1–5.

Wyatt v. Stickney, 344 F. Supp. 373 (M.D. Ala. 1972).

Yam, K. (2015, February 26). Blind man sees his wife for the first time in a decade after getting a bionic eye implant. *Huffington Post.* Retrieved from http://www.huffingtonpost.com/2015/02/26/allen-zderad-bionic-eye_n_6751962.html

Yu, M. Y., & Shim, W. (2009). Couples with schizophrenia "becoming like others" in South Korea: Marriage as part of a recovery process. *Family Process, 48*, 429–440.

Index

Although person-first language is important in acknowledging all people with disabilities, this index contains entries alphabetized by the particular disability.